# THE ESSEN

# COOKBOOK

Your Guide to Delicious Healing
and Digestive Wellness

# Nathan Perez

# Table of Contents

# INTRODUCTION

Welcome to the "EPI Diet Cookbook"! If you're holding this book, chances are you're on a quest for delicious, satisfying meals while navigating the complexities of managing Exocrine Pancreatic Insufficiency (EPI). Well, my friend, you've come to the right place.

First things first, let's address the elephant in the room: dealing with EPI isn't a walk in the park. It's more like a rollercoaster ride through a culinary maze, with unexpected twists and turns at every corner. But fear not! This cookbook is your trusty map, guiding you through the ups and downs of the EPI diet with grace, humor, and of course, mouthwatering recipes.

Now, before we dive headfirst into the culinary adventure awaiting us, let's take a moment to acknowledge the emotional rollercoaster that comes with managing a chronic condition like EPI. It's okay to feel frustrated, overwhelmed, or even downright hangry (that's hungry + angry, for the uninitiated). Trust me, I've been there too. But remember, you're not alone in this journey. Together, we'll navigate the twists and turns of the EPI diet with a dash of humor and a sprinkle of empathy.

In this cookbook, you'll find a treasure trove of recipes tailored specifically for EPI dieters. But hey, this isn't your typical bland and boring "diet food." No sir, we're talking about flavor-packed, drool-worthy dishes that will tantalize your taste buds and leave you craving more. From hearty breakfasts to satisfying mains and indulgent desserts, we've got you covered, every step of the way.

But wait, there's more! This cookbook isn't just about recipes. It's a culinary journey filled with tips, tricks, and insights to help you navigate the challenges of the EPI diet like a pro. We'll dive into essential ingredients, kitchen tools, and even decode those pesky food labels so you can make informed choices at the grocery store. Consider it your crash course in EPI-friendly cooking 101.

Now, I know what you're thinking. "But cooking with EPI sounds like a daunting task!" Trust me, I get it. Between managing symptoms, juggling appointments, and simply trying to live your best life, the last thing you want to do is spend hours slaving away in the kitchen. That's why I've made sure these recipes are not only delicious but also easy to whip up, even on your busiest days. Because let's face it, isn't nobody got time for complicated cooking shenanigans.

So, whether you're a seasoned chef or a kitchen newbie, I invite you to join me on this culinary adventure. Together, we'll laugh in the face of adversity, conquer culinary challenges, and savor every delicious bite along the way. Consider this cookbook your culinary companion, your kitchen confidante, and your ticket to culinary bliss in the world of EPI management.

Before we embark on this epic journey, I want to extend my heartfelt gratitude to you, dear reader. Thank you for trusting me to be your guide on this delicious adventure. Whether you're flipping through these pages in search of breakfast inspiration or drooling over dessert ideas, know that I'm right there with you, cheering you on every step of the way.

So, grab your apron, sharpen your knives, and let's get cooking! Together, we'll turn the challenges of EPI into culinary triumphs, one mouthwatering meal at a time.

Bon appétit!

Warmest regards,

# CHAPTER ONE

# THE BASICS OF THE EPI DIET

Exocrine Pancreatic Insufficiency (EPI) is not merely a condition; it's a journey that requires careful navigation through the complexities of diet and nutrition. In this chapter, we'll delve into the fundamental aspects of the EPI diet, exploring what EPI is, the pivotal role of diet in managing the condition, and the key principles that underpin an effective EPI diet plan.

## What is EPI? Understanding Exocrine Pancreatic Insufficiency

Let's start by demystifying EPI. At its core, Exocrine Pancreatic Insufficiency is a condition characterized by the inadequate production or secretion of digestive enzymes by the pancreas. These enzymes play a crucial role in breaking down fats, proteins, and carbohydrates from food, allowing for proper absorption and utilization of nutrients by the body.

When the pancreas fails to produce a sufficient amount of digestive enzymes, undigested food particles can pass through the digestive tract, leading to a range of gastrointestinal symptoms such as diarrhea, bloating, gas, and abdominal discomfort. Over time, untreated EPI can result in malnutrition, weight loss, and nutritional deficiencies, impacting overall health and quality of life.

EPI can have various underlying causes, including chronic pancreatitis, cystic fibrosis, pancreatic cancer, and certain gastrointestinal surgeries.

It can also develop as a result of aging, as the pancreas gradually loses its ability to produce enzymes efficiently.

Diagnosing EPI typically involves a combination of clinical symptoms, laboratory tests, and imaging studies. Common diagnostic tests include fecal elastase testing, which measures the level of pancreatic enzymes in the stool, and pancreatic function tests, which assess the pancreas's ability to secrete enzymes in response to stimulation.

Once diagnosed, the management of EPI revolves around addressing the underlying cause, relieving symptoms, and optimizing nutritional intake through dietary modifications and enzyme replacement therapy (ERT). Which brings us to our next point...

## The Role of Diet in Managing EPI

Diet plays a pivotal role in managing EPI, serving as a cornerstone of treatment alongside enzyme replacement therapy. The primary goal of dietary interventions in EPI is to minimize symptoms, optimize nutrient absorption, and promote overall digestive health.

One of the key challenges in managing EPI through diet is striking the right balance between ensuring adequate nutrient intake and avoiding foods that exacerbate symptoms. This often requires a tailored approach, as individual tolerance to certain foods can vary significantly among EPI patients.

## Key Principles of the EPI Diet

When it comes to dietary recommendations for EPI, several key principles come into play:

- **Moderate Fat Intake:** Since fat digestion is impaired in EPI, it's essential to limit dietary fat intake to reduce the burden on the pancreas. Opt for lean protein sources, such as poultry, fish, and legumes, and choose healthy fats from sources like avocados, nuts, and seeds in moderation.

- **Small, Frequent Meals:** Eating smaller, more frequent meals throughout the day can help alleviate digestive symptoms and promote better nutrient absorption. Aim for three main meals and two to three snacks spaced evenly throughout the day to prevent overloading the digestive system.

- **Focus on Easily Digestible Foods:** Choose foods that are easy to digest and gentle on the stomach, such as cooked vegetables, well-cooked grains, and tender proteins. Steer clear of tough, fibrous foods that may be harder to break down and digest.

- **Enzyme Replacement Therapy (ERT):** Enzyme replacement therapy is a cornerstone of EPI management, helping to compensate for the deficient pancreatic enzymes and improve digestion. Take enzyme supplements with meals and snacks as directed by your healthcare provider to enhance nutrient absorption and reduce symptoms.

- **Hydration:** Adequate hydration is essential for maintaining digestive health and preventing constipation, a common symptom of EPI. Aim to drink plenty of water throughout the day and limit intake of caffeinated and alcoholic beverages, which can exacerbate dehydration.

- **Balanced Nutrition:** Despite the challenges posed by EPI, it's important to strive for a balanced and varied diet that provides essential nutrients for overall health and well-being. Work with a registered dietitian or nutritionist to develop a personalized meal plan that meets your individual nutritional needs and dietary preferences.

By incorporating these key principles into your daily routine, you can effectively manage EPI symptoms, optimize nutrient absorption, and improve overall digestive health. Remember, managing EPI is a journey, and finding the right dietary approach may require some trial and error. Be patient with yourself, stay proactive in your approach to diet and nutrition, and don't hesitate to seek support from healthcare professionals and support groups along the way.

In the next chapters, we'll delve deeper into practical strategies for implementing the EPI diet, from stocking your pantry with EPI-friendly ingredients to whipping up delicious and nutritious meals that support digestive health and overall well-being. So, buckle up and get ready to embark on a delicious culinary adventure designed specifically for EPI warriors like you. Together, we'll navigate the twists and turns of the EPI diet with confidence, compassion, and a sprinkle of culinary creativity.

# CHAPTER TWO

# ESSENTIAL INGREDIENTS AND KITCHEN TOOLS

Creating delicious and nourishing meals while managing Exocrine Pancreatic Insufficiency (EPI) requires more than just culinary skills—it also involves having the right ingredients and tools at your disposal. In this chapter, we'll explore the essential ingredients for stocking your EPI-friendly pantry, must-have kitchen tools for EPI cooking, and tips for deciphering food labels to make informed choices.

## Stocking Your EPI-Friendly Pantry

A well-stocked pantry is the backbone of any successful cooking endeavor, and the same holds true for managing EPI. When it comes to stocking your EPI-friendly pantry, focus on ingredients that are easy to digest, nutrient-rich, and versatile enough to create a wide range of delicious dishes.

Here are some essential ingredients to keep on hand:

- **Low-Fat Proteins:** Opt for lean protein sources such as skinless poultry, fish, tofu, and legumes. These protein-rich foods are easier to digest and provide essential amino acids for muscle repair and overall health.

- **Whole Grains:** Choose whole grains such as brown rice, quinoa, oats, and whole wheat pasta. These fiber-rich grains provide sustained energy and promote digestive health by supporting regular bowel movements.

- **Cooking Oils:** Use heart-healthy oils such as olive oil, avocado oil, and coconut oil for cooking and dressing salads. These oils are rich in monounsaturated fats and antioxidants, which support cardiovascular health and reduce inflammation.

- **Canned and Frozen Fruits and Vegetables:** Stock up on canned and frozen fruits and vegetables to ensure you always have nutritious options on hand. Look for varieties without added sugars or sauces, and rinse canned vegetables to reduce sodium content.

- **Low-FODMAP Foods:** Many EPI patients also experience symptoms of irritable bowel syndrome (IBS), which can be exacerbated by high-FODMAP foods. Consider incorporating low-FODMAP options such as carrots, cucumbers, bell peppers, and strawberries into your diet to minimize digestive discomfort.

- **Enzyme Supplements:** Enzyme replacement therapy (ERT) is a crucial aspect of managing EPI, so be sure to have an ample supply of enzyme supplements on hand. Take enzyme capsules with meals and snacks as directed by your healthcare provider to support digestion and nutrient absorption.

By keeping these essential ingredients in your pantry, you'll be well-equipped to whip up delicious and nutritious meals that support your digestive health and overall well-being.

## Must-Have Kitchen Tools for EPI Cooking

In addition to stocking your pantry with EPI-friendly ingredients, having the right kitchen tools can streamline meal preparation and make cooking more enjoyable. Here are some must-have kitchen tools for EPI cooking:

- **Blender or Food Processor:** A high-quality blender or food processor is essential for pureeing soups, sauces, and smoothies to achieve a smooth and easily digestible consistency.

- **Non-Stick Cookware:** Invest in non-stick pots and pans to minimize the need for added fats and oils when cooking. Non-stick cookware also makes cleaning up a breeze, saving you time and effort in the kitchen.

- **Sharp Knives:** A set of sharp knives is indispensable for chopping, slicing, and dicing fruits, vegetables, and proteins with precision and ease. Keep your knives sharp and well-maintained to prevent accidents and ensure efficient meal preparation.

- **Steamer Basket:** A steamer basket is a versatile tool for gently cooking vegetables, seafood, and grains while preserving their natural flavors and nutrients. Steaming is a gentle cooking method that helps retain moisture and promotes easy digestion.

- **Measuring Cups and Spoons:** Accurate measurement is key to successful cooking, especially when following recipes or dietary guidelines. Invest in a set of measuring cups and spoons to ensure consistency and accuracy in your cooking endeavors.

- **Food Scale:** A food scale is helpful for portion control and accurate measurement of ingredients, particularly when following dietary recommendations or tracking nutrient intake.

- **Slow Cooker or Instant Pot:** A slow cooker or Instant Pot is a convenient tool for preparing hearty and nutritious meals with minimal hands-on effort. These versatile appliances are ideal for cooking soups, stews, and braises, allowing you to set it and forget it while flavors meld and develop.

By outfitting your kitchen with these essential tools, you'll be well-prepared to tackle the challenges of EPI cooking with confidence and ease.

## Understanding Food Labels: Tips for Making Informed Choices

Navigating the grocery store aisles can be daunting, especially when trying to decipher food labels and make informed choices for managing EPI. Here are some tips for understanding food labels and selecting EPI-friendly foods:

- **Check the Ingredient List:** Start by reviewing the ingredient list to identify any potential triggers or problematic ingredients. Look for whole, minimally processed foods with simple ingredient lists and avoid products containing artificial additives, preservatives, and high-FODMAP ingredients.

- **Pay Attention to Serving Size:** Be mindful of serving sizes listed on food labels, as they can vary significantly from product to product. Adjust portion sizes accordingly to ensure you're

11

consuming an appropriate amount of nutrients and calories for your individual needs.

- **Look for Low-Fat Options:** Opt for low-fat or reduced-fat versions of dairy products, meats, and packaged foods whenever possible to minimize the burden on your digestive system. Choose lean protein sources and limit intake of high-fat foods that may exacerbate EPI symptoms.

- **Monitor Sodium Content:** Keep an eye on the sodium content of packaged foods, as excessive salt intake can contribute to bloating, fluid retention, and high blood pressure. Choose low-sodium or sodium-free options and use herbs, spices, and other flavorings to enhance taste without relying on salt.

- **Check for Added Sugars:** Avoid products with added sugars, sweeteners, and syrups, which can contribute to digestive discomfort and destabilize blood sugar levels. Instead, opt for naturally sweetened foods such as fresh fruits or choose products sweetened with alternative sweeteners in moderation.

- **Consider Food Sensitivities:** If you have additional dietary restrictions or food sensitivities beyond EPI, such as lactose intolerance or gluten sensitivity, be sure to check food labels for potential allergens or trigger ingredients. Look for products labeled as "dairy-free," "gluten-free," or "allergen-free" to accommodate your specific dietary needs.

By becoming a savvy label reader and making informed choices at the grocery store, you can build a pantry stocked with EPI-friendly foods that support your health and well-being.

# CHAPTER THREE

# EPI-FRIENDLY FOODS

## Lean Proteins

| Food Name | Portion Size | Calories | Protein (g) | Fat (g) | Carbohydrates (g) | Fiber (g) |
|-----------|--------------|----------|-------------|---------|-------------------|-----------|
| Bison | 3 oz | 143 | 24 | 3 | 0 | 0 |
| Chicken (Thigh) | 3 oz | 177 | 26 | 7.7 | 0 | 0 |
| Crab | 3 oz | 98 | 20 | 1.3 | 0 | 0 |
| Duck | 3 oz | 155 | 19 | 7.3 | 0 | 0 |
| Elk | 3 oz | 138 | 25 | 3 | 0 | 0 |
| Emu | 3 oz | 125 | 22 | 3 | 0 | 0 |
| Fish (Cod) | 3 oz | 89 | 20 | 0.7 | 0 | 0 |
| Goose | 3 oz | 172 | 23 | 8.3 | 0 | 0 |
| Haddock | 3 oz | 95 | 20 | 0.7 | 0 | 0 |
| Halibut | 3 oz | 94 | 20 | 1 | 0 | 0 |
| Kangaroo | 3 oz | 99 | 23 | 1 | 0 | 0 |
| Lean Beef (Sirloin) | 3 oz | 147 | 25 | 4.5 | 0 | 0 |

| | | | | | |
|---|---|---|---|---|---|
| Lean Pork (Tenderloin) | 3 oz | 122 | 22 | 3 | 0 | 0 |
| Lobster | 3 oz | 89 | 17 | 0.9 | 0 | 0 |
| Mahi-mahi | 3 oz | 85 | 18 | 0.6 | 0 | 0 |
| Octopus | 3 oz | 139 | 25 | 2 | 2 | 0 |
| Ostrich | 3 oz | 140 | 26 | 3 | 0 | 0 |
| Pheasant | 3 oz | 149 | 27 | 3.6 | 0 | 0 |
| Quail | 3 oz | 134 | 21 | 4.5 | 0 | 0 |
| Rabbit | 3 oz | 147 | 28 | 3.5 | 0 | 0 |
| Salmon (Wild-caught) | 3 oz | 155 | 22 | 7 | 0 | 0 |
| Shrimp | 3 oz | 84 | 18 | 1.2 | 0 | 0 |
| Skinless Chicken Breast | 3 oz | 128 | 26 | 2.7 | 0 | 0 |
| Snapper | 3 oz | 94 | 20 | 1 | 0 | 0 |
| Swordfish | 3 oz | 155 | 23 | 7 | 0 | 0 |
| Tilapia | 3 oz | 109 | 23 | 1.8 | 0 | 0 |
| Tuna (Canned in Water) | 3 oz | 99 | 22 | 0.6 | 0 | 0 |
| Turkey (Thigh) | 3 oz | 192 | 26 | 9.2 | 0 | 0 |
| Turkey Breast | 3 oz | 135 | 26 | 3 | 0 | 0 |

| | | | | | | |
|---|---|---|---|---|---|---|
| Venison | 3 oz | 158 | 26 | 4 | 0 | 0 |

## Low-Fat Dairy

| Food Name | Portion Size | Calories | Protein (g) | Fat (g) | Carbohydrates (g) | Fiber (g) |
|---|---|---|---|---|---|---|
| Fat-Free American Cheese | 1 slice | 30 | 5 | 0 | 2 | 0 |
| Fat-Free Cheddar Cheese | 1 oz | 40 | 9 | 0 | 1 | 0 |
| Fat-Free Cream Cheese | 1 oz | 30 | 2 | 0 | 6 | 0 |
| Fat-Free Creamer | 1 tbsp | 10 | 0 | 0 | 1 | 0 |
| Fat-Free Creamy Salad Dressing | 2 tbsp | 35 | 1 | 0 | 7 | 0 |
| Fat-Free Evaporated Milk | 1/2 cup | 100 | 9 | 0 | 15 | 0 |
| Fat-Free Greek Yogurt | 6 oz | 100 | 18 | 0 | 6 | 0 |
| Fat-Free Half-and-Half | 2 tbsp | 20 | 1 | 0 | 3 | 0 |
| Fat-Free Ice Cream | 1/2 cup | 100 | 3 | 0 | 20 | 0 |
| Fat-Free Mayo | 1 tbsp | 11 | 0 | 0 | 2 | 0 |
| Fat-Free Milk | 1 tbsp | 32 | 3 | 0 | 4 | 0 |

| | | | | | |
|---|---|---|---|---|---|
| Powder | | | | | |
| Fat-Free Mozzarella Cheese | 1 oz | 41 | 8 | 0 | 1 | 0 |
| Fat-Free Pudding | 1/2 cup | 70 | 1 | 0 | 16 | 0 |
| Fat-Free Ricotta Cheese | 1/2 cup | 140 | 28 | 0 | 6 | 0 |
| Low-Fat Blue Cheese | 1 oz | 50 | 6 | 2.5 | 1 | 0 |
| Low-Fat Buttermilk | 1 cup | 98 | 8 | 2 | 12 | 0 |
| Low-Fat Cheddar Cheese | 1 oz | 50 | 7 | 2 | 1 | 0 |
| Low-Fat Cottage Cheese | 1/2 cup | 81 | 14 | 1 | 3 | 0 |
| Low-Fat Cream Cheese | 1 tbsp | 30 | 1 | 1.5 | 1 | 0 |
| Low-Fat Feta Cheese | 1 oz | 35 | 6 | 1 | 1 | 0 |
| Low-Fat Frozen Yogurt | 1/2 cup | 100 | 3 | 1 | 20 | 0 |
| Low-Fat Gouda Cheese | 1 oz | 65 | 7 | 2.5 | 1 | 0 |
| Low-Fat Kefir | 1 cup | 110 | 11 | 2.5 | 12 | 0 |
| Low-Fat Milk | 1 cup | 102 | 8 | 2 | 12 | 0 |

| | | | | | |
|---|---|---|---|---|---|
| Low-Fat Parmesan Cheese | 1 tbsp | 22 | 2 | 1 | 1 | 0 |
| Low-Fat Sour Cream | 1 tbsp | 20 | 1 | 1 | 2 | 0 |
| Low-Fat String Cheese | 1 piece | 50 | 6 | 1.5 | 1 | 0 |
| Low-Fat Swiss Cheese | 1 oz | 50 | 7 | 2 | 1 | 0 |
| Low-Fat Yogurt (Plain) | 6 oz | 93 | 9 | 2 | 12 | 0 |
| Skim Milk | 1 cup | 83 | 8 | 0.2 | 12 | 0 |

## Healthy Carbohydrate

| Food Name | Portion Size | Calories | Protein (g) | Fat (g) | Carbohydrates (g) | Fiber (g) |
|---|---|---|---|---|---|---|
| Sweet Potato | 1 medium | 103 | 2 | 0 | 24 | 4 |
| Brown Rice | 1/2 cup | 108 | 2 | 0.4 | 22.5 | 1.8 |
| Quinoa | 1/2 cup | 111 | 4 | 1.8 | 19.7 | 2.6 |
| Oats (Steel-Cut) | 1/4 cup | 150 | 7 | 3 | 27 | 4 |
| Barley | 1/2 cup | 97 | 2 | 0.3 | 22.8 | 3.6 |
| Bulgur | 1/2 cup | 76 | 3 | 0.2 | 17.3 | 4 |
| Whole Wheat Pasta | 1/2 cup | 87 | 3 | 0.8 | 17.3 | 2 |

| | | | | | | |
|---|---|---|---|---|---|---|
| Buckwheat | 1/2 cup | 154 | 5 | 1.5 | 32.5 | 4 |
| Millet | 1/2 cup | 189 | 6 | 1.7 | 37.6 | 2.3 |
| Amaranth | 1/2 cup | 125 | 4 | 2 | 23 | 3 |
| Whole Grain Bread | 1 slice | 69 | 3 | 0.9 | 12.4 | 1.9 |
| Rye Bread | 1 slice | 83 | 3 | 0.7 | 17.1 | 1.9 |
| Whole Wheat Tortilla | 1 medium | 104 | 3 | 1.6 | 18.5 | 2.4 |
| Whole Grain Crackers | 6 crackers | 120 | 3 | 3 | 20 | 3 |
| Whole Grain Cereal | 1 cup | 120 | 4 | 1 | 24 | 4 |
| Whole Grain Bagel | 1 medium | 245 | 9 | 1.5 | 49 | 4 |
| Whole Grain English Muffin | 1 medium | 134 | 4 | 1 | 26 | 3 |
| Whole Wheat Pita Bread | 1 medium | 80 | 3 | 0.5 | 17 | 2 |
| Brown Rice Cake | 1 cake | 35 | 1 | 0.3 | 7 | 0.6 |
| Whole Grain Pretzels | 1 oz | 110 | 3 | 1 | 22 | 2 |
| Whole Wheat Couscous | 1/2 cup | 100 | 4 | 0 | 22 | 2 |
| Whole Grain Waffles | 2 waffles | 160 | 5 | 3 | 28 | 4 |
| Whole Grain Pancakes | 2 pancakes | 220 | 6 | 4 | 38 | 4 |
| Whole Grain | 1 | 134 | 4 | 1 | 26 | 3 |

| Food Name | Portion Size | Calories | Protein (g) | Fat (g) | Carbohydrates (g) | Fiber (g) |
|---|---|---|---|---|---|---|
| English Muffin | medium | | | | | |
| Whole Grain Breadsticks | 1 stick | 80 | 2 | 1 | 16 | 2 |
| Whole Grain Crackers | 6 crackers | 120 | 3 | 3 | 20 | 3 |
| Whole Grain Rice | 1/2 cup | 108 | 2 | 0.5 | 22.4 | 1.8 |
| Whole Grain Baguette | 1 medium | 100 | 3 | 0.5 | 20 | 2 |
| Whole Grain English Muffin | 1 medium | 134 | 4 | 1 | 26 | 3 |

## Fruits and Vegetables

| Food Name | Portion Size | Calories | Protein (g) | Fat (g) | Carbohydrates (g) | Fiber (g) |
|---|---|---|---|---|---|---|
| Acorn Squash | 1 cup | 115 | 1.8 | 0.4 | 30.6 | 9 |
| Arugula | 1 cup | 5 | 0.5 | 0.1 | 0.7 | 0.3 |
| Asparagus | 1 cup | 27 | 2.9 | 0.2 | 5.2 | 2.8 |
| Beets | 1 cup | 58 | 2 | 0.2 | 13 | 3.8 |
| Bell Peppers | 1 medium | 24 | 0.9 | 0.2 | 5.5 | 2.1 |
| Broccoli | 1 cup | 55 | 4.7 | 0.6 | 10.1 | 4.6 |
| Brussels Sprouts | 1 cup | 38 | 3 | 0.3 | 8 | 3.3 |
| Butternut Squash | 1 cup | 82 | 1.8 | 0.2 | 21.5 | 6 |
| Cabbage | 1 cup | 22 | 1.1 | 0.1 | 5.2 | 2.2 |
| Carrots | 1 medium | 25 | 0.6 | 0.1 | 5.8 | 1.7 |
| Cauliflower | 1 cup | 25 | 2 | 0.3 | 5.3 | 2.1 |
| Celery | 1 | 6 | 0.3 | 0 | 1.2 | 0.6 |

|  |  |  |  |  |  |  |
|---|---|---|---|---|---|---|
|  | mediu m |  |  |  |  |  |
| Cucumber | 1 mediu m | 45 | 2 | 0.3 | 8 | 1.2 |
| Eggplant | 1 cup | 20 | 0.8 | 0.2 | 4.8 | 2.5 |
| Garlic | 1 clove | 4 | 0.2 | 0 | 1 | 0.1 |
| Green Beans | 1 cup | 31 | 1.8 | 0.2 | 7.1 | 3.4 |
| Green Peas | 1 cup | 117 | 8 | 0.6 | 21 | 8 |
| Kale | 1 cup | 33 | 2.2 | 0.5 | 6.7 | 1.3 |
| Mushrooms | 1 cup | 15 | 2.2 | 0.2 | 2.3 | 0.7 |
| Onions | 1 mediu m | 44 | 1.1 | 0 | 10.1 | 1.9 |
| Pumpkin | 1 cup | 49 | 2 | 0.2 | 12 | 3 |
| Romaine Lettuce | 1 cup | 8 | 0.5 | 0 | 1.5 | 1 |
| Snow Peas | 1 cup | 26 | 1.6 | 0.2 | 4.8 | 1.6 |
| Spinach | 1 cup | 7 | 0.9 | 0.1 | 1.1 | 0.7 |
| Sugar Snap Peas | 1 cup | 41 | 2.6 | 0.2 | 8.6 | 3 |
| Sweet Bell Peppers | 1 mediu m | 24 | 1 | 0.2 | 6 | 2 |
| Tomatillos | 1 mediu m | 11 | 0.6 | 0.1 | 2.4 | 0.9 |
| Tomatoes | 1 mediu m | 22 | 1.1 | 0.2 | 4.8 | 1.5 |
| Zucchini | 1 mediu m | 33 | 2 | 0.6 | 6 | 2 |

# BREAKFAST RECIPES

## Savory Breakfast Quinoa Bowl

Prep Time: 5 mins

Total Time: 20 mins

Servings: 2 bowls

**Ingredients:**

- 1 cup quinoa, rinsed
- 2 cups water or low-sodium vegetable broth
- 1 tablespoon olive oil
- 1/2 onion, diced
- 1 bell pepper, diced
- 2 cloves garlic, minced
- 2 cups fresh spinach
- Salt and pepper to taste
- 1 avocado, sliced
- 2 poached eggs (optional)
- Fresh herbs for garnish (e.g., parsley, chives)

**Directions:**

1. In a medium saucepan, combine quinoa and water or broth. Bring to a boil, then reduce heat to low, cover, and simmer for 15 minutes, or until quinoa is cooked and liquid is absorbed.

2. While quinoa is cooking, heat olive oil in a skillet over medium heat. Add diced onion and bell pepper, and sauté until softened, about 5 minutes. Add minced garlic and cook for an additional minute.

3. Add fresh spinach to the skillet and cook until wilted. Season with salt and pepper to taste.
4. Divide cooked quinoa between two bowls. Top with sautéed vegetables, sliced avocado, and poached eggs (if using).
5. Garnish with fresh herbs and serve hot.

**Nutrition Facts (per serving):**

- Calories: 395
- Protein: 13g
- Fat: 18g
- Carbohydrates: 50g
- Fiber: 9g

# Blueberry Almond Chia Pudding

Prep Time: 5 mins

Total Time: 4 hours (chilling time)

Servings: 2 servings

**Ingredients:**

- 1/4 cup chia seeds
- 1 cup unsweetened almond milk
- 1/2 teaspoon vanilla extract
- 1 tablespoon maple syrup or honey (optional)
- 1/2 cup fresh blueberries
- 2 tablespoons sliced almonds

**Directions:**

1. In a mixing bowl, combine chia seeds, almond milk, vanilla extract, and maple syrup or honey (if using). Stir well to combine.

2. Cover the bowl and refrigerate for at least 4 hours or overnight, until the mixture has thickened to a pudding-like consistency.

3. Before serving, stir the chia pudding to redistribute the seeds. Divide the pudding between two serving glasses or bowls.

4. Top each serving with fresh blueberries and sliced almonds.

5. Serve chilled.

**Nutrition Facts (per serving):**

- Calories: 245
- Protein: 6g
- Fat: 14g
- Carbohydrates: 25g
- Fiber: 10g

# Spinach and Feta Omelette

Prep Time: 5 mins

Total Time: 10 mins

Servings: 1 omelette

**Ingredients:**

- 2 large eggs
- 1 tablespoon water or milk
- Salt and pepper to taste
- 1 teaspoon olive oil
- 1 cup fresh spinach
- 2 tablespoons crumbled feta cheese

**Directions:**

1. In a small bowl, whisk together eggs, water or milk, salt, and pepper until well combined.

2. Heat olive oil in a non-stick skillet over medium heat. Add fresh spinach and cook until wilted, about 1-2 minutes.

3. Pour the egg mixture into the skillet, tilting the pan to distribute the eggs evenly.

4. Cook the omelette for 2-3 minutes, or until the edges start to set and the bottom is lightly golden.

5. Sprinkle crumbled feta cheese over one half of the omelette. Fold the other half over the filling.

6. Cook for an additional 1-2 minutes, or until the cheese is melted and the eggs are cooked through.

7. Slide the omelette onto a plate and serve hot.

**Nutrition Facts (per serving):**

- Calories: 250
- Protein: 19g
- Fat: 17g
- Carbohydrates: 3g
- Fiber: 1g

## Avocado Toast with Smoked Salmon

Prep Time: 5 mins

Total Time: 10 mins

Servings: 2 slices

**Ingredients:**

- 2 slices whole grain bread, toasted
- 1 ripe avocado
- Juice of 1/2 lemon
- Salt and pepper to taste

- 2 ounces smoked salmon
- 1 tablespoon capers
- Fresh dill for garnish

**Directions:**

1. In a small bowl, mash the ripe avocado with lemon juice, salt, and pepper until smooth and creamy.
2. Spread the mashed avocado evenly onto the toasted bread slices.
3. Top each slice with smoked salmon and sprinkle with capers.
4. Garnish with fresh dill leaves.
5. Serve immediately.

**Nutrition Facts (per serving):**

- Calories: 230
- Protein: 13g
- Fat: 13g
- Carbohydrates: 18g
- Fiber: 6g

# Greek Yogurt Parfait with Berries and Granola

Prep Time: 5 mins

Total Time: 5 mins

Servings: 1 parfait

**Ingredients:**

- 1/2 cup plain Greek yogurt
- 1/4 cup fresh mixed berries (e.g., strawberries, blueberries, raspberries)
- 1/4 cup granola (choose a low-fat, low-sugar option)

- 1 tablespoon honey or maple syrup (optional)

**Directions:**

1. In a serving glass or bowl, layer Greek yogurt, mixed berries, and granola.
2. Drizzle honey or maple syrup over the top, if desired.
3. Repeat layers until the glass or bowl is filled.
4. Serve immediately as a nutritious and satisfying breakfast option.

**Nutrition Facts (per serving):**

- Calories: 250
- Protein: 15g
- Fat: 5g
- Carbohydrates: 35g
- Fiber: 5g

# Egg and Vegetable Breakfast Burrito

Prep Time: 10 mins

Total Time: 20 mins

Servings: 2 burritos

**Ingredients:**

- 4 large eggs
- 1/4 cup diced bell peppers (any color)
- 1/4 cup diced onions
- 1/4 cup diced tomatoes
- 1/4 cup diced mushrooms
- 2 whole grain tortillas
- Salt and pepper to taste

- 1/4 cup shredded cheese (optional)
- Salsa and avocado slices for serving

**Directions:**

1. In a mixing bowl, whisk the eggs until well beaten. Season with salt and pepper to taste.
2. Heat a non-stick skillet over medium heat. Add diced bell peppers, onions, tomatoes, and mushrooms, and sauté until softened, about 5 minutes.
3. Pour the beaten eggs over the cooked vegetables in the skillet. Cook, stirring occasionally, until the eggs are set and scrambled.
4. Divide the scrambled eggs and vegetable mixture between two whole grain tortillas. Sprinkle shredded cheese on top if desired.
5. Roll up the tortillas to form burritos, folding in the sides as you go.
6. Serve the breakfast burritos with salsa and avocado slices on the side.

**Nutrition Facts (per serving):**

- Calories: 320
- Protein: 17g
- Fat: 14g
- Carbohydrates: 30g
- Fiber: 6g

# Quinoa Breakfast Porridge

Prep Time: 5 mins

Total Time: 15 mins

Servings: 2 bowls

**Ingredients:**

- 1/2 cup quinoa, rinsed
- 1 cup almond milk
- 1/2 teaspoon ground cinnamon
- 1 tablespoon maple syrup or honey
- 1/4 cup chopped nuts (e.g., almonds, walnuts)
- Fresh fruit for topping (e.g., berries, sliced banana)

**Directions:**

1. In a saucepan, combine quinoa and almond milk. Bring to a boil, then reduce heat to low, cover, and simmer for 10-12 minutes, or until quinoa is cooked and liquid is absorbed.
2. Stir in ground cinnamon and maple syrup or honey. Cook for an additional 2-3 minutes, stirring occasionally.
3. Divide the quinoa porridge between two bowls. Top with chopped nuts and fresh fruit.
4. Serve hot and enjoy!

**Nutrition Facts (per serving):**

- Calories: 320
- Protein: 9g
- Fat: 12g
- Carbohydrates: 45g
- Fiber: 6g

## Sweet Potato and Black Bean Breakfast Hash

Prep Time: 10 mins

Total Time: 30 mins

Servings: 2 servings

**Ingredients:**

- 1 large sweet potato, diced
- 1/2 onion, diced
- 1 bell pepper, diced
- 1 cup cooked black beans
- 1 teaspoon ground cumin
- 1/2 teaspoon smoked paprika
- Salt and pepper to taste
- 2 eggs
- Fresh cilantro for garnish

**Directions:**

1. Heat olive oil in a skillet over medium heat. Add diced sweet potato and cook until tender, about 10-12 minutes.
2. Add diced onion and bell pepper to the skillet and cook until softened, about 5 minutes.
3. Stir in cooked black beans, ground cumin, smoked paprika, salt, and pepper. Cook for an additional 2-3 minutes, until heated through.
4. Create two wells in the hash mixture and crack an egg into each well.
5. Cover the skillet and cook for 5-7 minutes, or until the eggs are cooked to your desired doneness.
6. Garnish with fresh cilantro and serve hot.

**Nutrition Facts (per serving):**

- Calories: 320
- Protein: 15g
- Fat: 10g
- Carbohydrates: 45g
- Fiber: 10g

# Coconut Chia Seed Pudding

Prep Time: 5 mins

Total Time: 4 hours (chilling time)

Servings: 2 servings

**Ingredients:**

- 1/4 cup chia seeds
- 1 cup coconut milk
- 1 tablespoon maple syrup or honey (optional)
- 1/2 teaspoon vanilla extract
- 1/4 cup toasted coconut flakes

**Directions:**

1. In a mixing bowl, combine chia seeds, coconut milk, maple syrup or honey (if using), and vanilla extract. Stir well to combine.
2. Cover the bowl and refrigerate for at least 4 hours or overnight, until the mixture has thickened to a pudding-like consistency.
3. Before serving, stir the chia pudding to redistribute the seeds. Divide the pudding between two serving glasses or bowls.
4. Top each serving with toasted coconut flakes.
5. Serve chilled and enjoy!

**Nutrition Facts (per serving):**

- Calories: 280
- Protein: 5g
- Fat: 22g
- Carbohydrates: 20g
- Fiber: 10g

## Quinoa Breakfast Bowl

Prep Time: 5 mins

Total Time: 20 mins

Servings: 2 bowls

**Ingredients:**

- 1/2 cup quinoa, rinsed
- 1 cup water or vegetable broth
- 1 tablespoon olive oil
- 1/2 onion, diced
- 1 bell pepper, diced
- 2 cups fresh spinach
- 4 large eggs
- Salt and pepper to taste
- Fresh herbs for garnish (e.g., parsley, chives)

**Directions:**

1. In a saucepan, bring water or vegetable broth to a boil. Add quinoa, reduce heat to low, cover, and simmer for 15 minutes, or until quinoa is cooked and liquid is absorbed.

2. While quinoa is cooking, heat olive oil in a skillet over medium heat. Add diced onion and bell pepper, and sauté until softened, about 5 minutes.
3. Add fresh spinach to the skillet and cook until wilted. Season with salt and pepper to taste.
4. In a separate non-stick skillet, fry the eggs to your desired doneness.
5. Divide cooked quinoa between two bowls. Top with sautéed vegetables and fried eggs.
6. Garnish with fresh herbs and serve hot.

**Nutrition Facts (per serving):**

- Calories: 320
- Protein: 17g
- Fat: 14g
- Carbohydrates: 30g
- Fiber: 6g

## Smoked Salmon and Avocado Toast

Prep Time: 5 mins

Total Time: 10 mins

Servings: 2 slices

**Ingredients:**

- 2 slices whole grain bread, toasted
- 1 ripe avocado
- Juice of 1/2 lemon
- Salt and pepper to taste
- 2 ounces smoked salmon

- 2 tablespoons capers

**Directions:**

1. In a small bowl, mash the ripe avocado with lemon juice, salt, and pepper until smooth and creamy.
2. Spread the mashed avocado evenly onto the toasted bread slices.
3. Top each slice with smoked salmon and sprinkle with capers.
4. Serve immediately.

**Nutrition Facts (per serving):**

- Calories: 280
- Protein: 15g
- Fat: 12g
- Carbohydrates: 30g
- Fiber: 7g

# Greek Yogurt Parfait

Prep Time: 5 mins

Total Time: 5 mins

Servings: 2 servings

**Ingredients:**

- 1 cup plain Greek yogurt
- 1/2 cup fresh mixed berries (e.g., strawberries, blueberries, raspberries)
- 1/4 cup granola (choose a low-fat, low-sugar option)
- 1 tablespoon honey or maple syrup (optional)

**Directions:**

1. In a serving glass or bowl, layer Greek yogurt, mixed berries, and granola.
2. Drizzle honey or maple syrup over the top, if desired.
3. Serve immediately.

**Nutrition Facts (per serving):**

- Calories: 250
- Protein: 15g
- Fat: 5g
- Carbohydrates: 35g
- Fiber: 5g

## Spinach and Feta Omelette

Prep Time: 5 mins

Total Time: 10 mins

Servings: 1 omelette

**Ingredients:**

- 2 large eggs
- 1 tablespoon water or milk
- Salt and pepper to taste
- 1 teaspoon olive oil
- 1 cup fresh spinach
- 2 tablespoons crumbled feta cheese

**Directions:**

1. In a small bowl, whisk together eggs, water or milk, salt, and pepper until well combined.
2. Heat olive oil in a non-stick skillet over medium heat. Add fresh spinach and cook until wilted, about 1-2 minutes.

3. Pour the egg mixture into the skillet, tilting the pan to distribute the eggs evenly.

4. Cook the omelette for 2-3 minutes, or until the edges start to set and the bottom is lightly golden.

5. Sprinkle crumbled feta cheese over one half of the omelette. Fold the other half over the filling.

6. Cook for an additional 1-2 minutes, or until the cheese is melted and the eggs are cooked through.

7. Slide the omelette onto a plate and serve hot.

**Nutrition Facts (per serving):**

- Calories: 280
- Protein: 19g
- Fat: 17g
- Carbohydrates: 3g
- Fiber: 1g

# Blueberry Almond Chia Pudding

Prep Time: 5 mins

Total Time: 4 hours (chilling time)

Servings: 2 servings

**Ingredients:**

- 1/4 cup chia seeds
- 1 cup unsweetened almond milk
- 1/2 teaspoon vanilla extract
- 1 tablespoon maple syrup or honey (optional)
- 1/2 cup fresh blueberries
- 2 tablespoons sliced almonds

**Directions:**

1. In a mixing bowl, combine chia seeds, almond milk, vanilla extract, and maple syrup or honey (if using). Stir well to combine.

2. Cover the bowl and refrigerate for at least 4 hours or overnight, until the mixture has thickened to a pudding-like consistency.

3. Before serving, stir the chia pudding to redistribute the seeds. Divide the pudding between two serving glasses or bowls.

4. Top each serving with fresh blueberries and sliced almonds.

5. Serve chilled.

**Nutrition Facts (per serving):**

- Calories: 245
- Protein: 6g
- Fat: 14g
- Carbohydrates: 25g
- Fiber: 10g

## Spinach and Mushroom Breakfast Frittata

Prep Time: 10 mins

Total Time: 25 mins

Servings: 4 servings

**Ingredients:**

- 6 large eggs
- 1/4 cup milk (or dairy-free alternative)
- Salt and pepper to taste
- 1 tablespoon olive oil
- 1/2 onion, diced

- 1 cup sliced mushrooms
- 2 cups fresh spinach
- 1/4 cup shredded cheese (optional)

**Directions:**

1. Preheat your oven to 350°F (175°C).
2. In a mixing bowl, whisk together eggs, milk, salt, and pepper until well combined.
3. Heat olive oil in an oven-safe skillet over medium heat. Add diced onion and sliced mushrooms, and cook until softened, about 5 minutes.
4. Add fresh spinach to the skillet and cook until wilted.
5. Pour the egg mixture over the cooked vegetables in the skillet. Stir gently to distribute the ingredients evenly.
6. Cook for 2-3 minutes, or until the edges start to set.
7. Sprinkle shredded cheese (if using) over the top of the frittata.
8. Transfer the skillet to the preheated oven and bake for 10-12 minutes, or until the eggs are set and the top is golden brown.
9. Remove from the oven and let cool for a few minutes before slicing and serving.

**Nutrition Facts (per serving):**

- Calories: 180
- Protein: 12g
- Fat: 11g
- Carbohydrates: 6g
- Fiber: 1g

# Overnight Oats with Berries and Almonds

Prep Time: 5 mins

Total Time: 8 hours (overnight chilling)

Servings: 2 servings

**Ingredients:**

- 1 cup old-fashioned rolled oats
- 1 cup almond milk (or dairy-free alternative)
- 1 tablespoon chia seeds
- 1/2 teaspoon vanilla extract
- 1 tablespoon maple syrup or honey
- 1/2 cup mixed berries (e.g., strawberries, blueberries, raspberries)
- 2 tablespoons sliced almonds

**Directions:**

1. In a mixing bowl or jar, combine rolled oats, almond milk, chia seeds, vanilla extract, and maple syrup or honey. Stir well to combine.

2. Cover the bowl or jar and refrigerate overnight, or for at least 8 hours.

3. Before serving, stir the overnight oats to mix well. If the mixture is too thick, you can add a splash of almond milk to reach your desired consistency.

4. Divide the overnight oats between two serving bowls.

5. Top each serving with mixed berries and sliced almonds.

6. Serve chilled and enjoy!

**Nutrition Facts (per serving):**

- Calories: 300

- Protein: 9g
- Fat: 12g
- Carbohydrates: 40g
- Fiber: 8g

## Turkey and Vegetable Breakfast Hash

Prep Time: 10 mins

Total Time: 25 mins

Servings: 2 servings

**Ingredients:**

- 2 tablespoons olive oil
- 1/2 onion, diced
- 1 bell pepper, diced
- 2 cups diced sweet potatoes
- 8 ounces cooked turkey breast, diced
- Salt and pepper to taste
- Fresh parsley for garnish

**Directions:**

1. Heat olive oil in a skillet over medium heat. Add diced onion and bell pepper, and cook until softened, about 5 minutes.
2. Add diced sweet potatoes to the skillet and cook until tender, about 10-12 minutes.
3. Stir in diced turkey breast and cook until heated through.
4. Season with salt and pepper to taste.
5. Divide the turkey and vegetable hash between two serving plates.
6. Garnish with fresh parsley and serve hot.

**Nutrition Facts (per serving):**

- Calories: 320
- Protein: 25g
- Fat: 10g
- Carbohydrates: 30g
- Fiber: 6g

## Green Breakfast Smoothie Bowl

Prep Time: 5 mins

Total Time: 5 mins

Servings: 1 bowl

**Ingredients:**

- 1 ripe banana, frozen
- 1 cup fresh spinach
- 1/2 cup frozen pineapple chunks
- 1/2 cup almond milk (or dairy-free alternative)
- 1 tablespoon chia seeds
- 2 tablespoons granola
- Fresh berries for topping

**Directions:**

1. In a blender, combine frozen banana, fresh spinach, frozen pineapple chunks, almond milk, and chia seeds. Blend until smooth and creamy.
2. Pour the smoothie into a serving bowl.
3. Top with granola and fresh berries.
4. Serve immediately and enjoy!

**Nutrition Facts (per serving):**

- Calories: 300
- Protein: 7g
- Fat: 10g
- Carbohydrates: 50g
- Fiber: 10g

# Avocado and Tomato Breakfast Toast

Prep Time: 5 mins

Total Time: 5 mins

Servings: 2 slices

**Ingredients:**

- 2 slices whole grain bread, toasted
- 1 ripe avocado
- 1 tomato, sliced
- Salt and pepper to taste
- Fresh basil leaves for garnish

**Directions:**

1. Mash the ripe avocado in a small bowl. Season with salt and pepper to taste.
2. Spread the mashed avocado evenly onto the toasted bread slices.
3. Top each slice with sliced tomatoes.
4. Garnish with fresh basil leaves.
5. Serve immediately.

**Nutrition Facts (per serving):**

- Calories: 200
- Protein: 5g

- Fat: 10g
- Carbohydrates: 25g
- Fiber: 8g

# LUNCH RECIPES

## Quinoa Salad with Grilled Chicken

Prep Time: 15 mins

Total Time: 30 mins

Servings: 4 servings

**Ingredients:**

- 1 cup quinoa
- 2 cups water or vegetable broth
- 2 boneless, skinless chicken breasts
- 2 tbsp olive oil
- 1 tsp garlic powder
- Salt and pepper to taste
- 1 cup diced cucumber
- 1 cup cherry tomatoes, halved
- 1/2 cup diced red onion
- 1/4 cup chopped fresh parsley
- 1/4 cup crumbled feta cheese (optional)
- 2 tbsp balsamic vinegar
- 1 tbsp lemon juice

**Directions:**

1. Rinse quinoa under cold water.
2. In a saucepan, bring water or vegetable broth to a boil.
3. Add quinoa, reduce heat to low, cover, and simmer for 15 minutes until quinoa is cooked and water is absorbed.
4. Preheat grill or grill pan over medium-high heat.

5. Brush chicken breasts with olive oil and season with garlic powder, salt, and pepper.

6. Grill chicken for 6-8 minutes per side until cooked through and no longer pink in the center.

7. Remove chicken from the grill and let it rest for 5 minutes before slicing.

8. In a large bowl, combine cooked quinoa, diced cucumber, cherry tomatoes, red onion, and chopped parsley.

9. Add crumbled feta cheese if using.

10. Drizzle balsamic vinegar and lemon juice over the salad and toss to combine.

11. Divide salad into serving bowls and top with sliced grilled chicken.

12. Serve warm or chilled and enjoy!

**Nutrition Facts (per serving):**

- Calories: 350
- Protein: 25g
- Fat: 12g
- Carbohydrates: 35g
- Fiber: 5g

# Salmon and Avocado Sushi Bowl

Prep Time: 20 mins

Total Time: 20 mins

Servings: 2 servings

**Ingredients:**

- 1 cup cooked sushi rice

- 2 salmon fillets, grilled or baked
- 1 avocado, sliced
- 1/2 cucumber, julienned
- 1/2 carrot, julienned
- 2 tbsp soy sauce
- 1 tbsp rice vinegar
- 1 tsp sesame oil
- 1 tsp sesame seeds
- Pickled ginger and wasabi for serving (optional)

**Directions:**

1. Divide cooked sushi rice into serving bowls.
2. Top with grilled or baked salmon fillets, sliced avocado, julienned cucumber, and carrot.
3. In a small bowl, whisk together soy sauce, rice vinegar, and sesame oil to make the dressing.
4. Drizzle dressing over the sushi bowls.
5. Sprinkle with sesame seeds.
6. Serve with pickled ginger and wasabi if desired.
7. Serve immediately and enjoy!

**Nutrition Facts (per serving):**

- Calories: 400
- Protein: 25g
- Fat: 20g
- Carbohydrates: 30g
- Fiber: 5g

# Mediterranean Chickpea Salad

Prep Time: 15 mins

Total Time: 15 mins

Servings: 4 servings

## Ingredients:

- 2 cans (15 oz each) chickpeas, drained and rinsed
- 1 cup diced cucumber
- 1 cup cherry tomatoes, halved
- 1/2 cup diced red onion
- 1/4 cup chopped fresh parsley
- 1/4 cup crumbled feta cheese (optional)
- 2 tbsp olive oil
- 1 tbsp lemon juice
- 1 tsp dried oregano
- Salt and pepper to taste

## Directions:

1. In a large bowl, combine chickpeas, diced cucumber, cherry tomatoes, red onion, and chopped parsley.
2. Add crumbled feta cheese if using.
3. In a small bowl, whisk together olive oil, lemon juice, dried oregano, salt, and pepper to make the dressing.
4. Drizzle dressing over the salad and toss to combine.
5. Serve immediately or refrigerate until ready to serve.
6. Serve chilled and enjoy!

## Nutrition Facts (per serving):

- Calories: 300
- Protein: 12g

- Fat: 12g
- Carbohydrates: 35g
- Fiber: 8g

## Turkey and Hummus Wrap

Prep Time: 10 mins

Total Time: 10 mins

Servings: 2 wraps

**Ingredients:**

- 4 whole grain tortilla wraps
- 8 slices deli turkey breast
- 1/2 cup hummus
- 1 cup mixed greens
- 1/2 cucumber, thinly sliced
- 1/4 cup shredded carrots
- Salt and pepper to taste

**Directions:**

1. Lay out tortilla wraps on a flat surface.
2. Spread hummus evenly onto each tortilla.
3. Place 2 slices of deli turkey breast onto each tortilla.
4. Top with mixed greens, cucumber slices, and shredded carrots.
5. Season with salt and pepper to taste.
6. Roll up each tortilla into a wrap.
7. Slice in half if desired and serve immediately.

**Nutrition Facts (per serving):**

- Calories: 300
- Protein: 20g

- Fat: 10g
- Carbohydrates: 30g
- Fiber: 8g

## Vegetable Stir-Fry with Tofu

Prep Time: 15 mins

Total Time: 25 mins

Servings: 4 servings

**Ingredients:**

- 1 block (14 oz) extra-firm tofu, pressed and cubed
- 2 tbsp soy sauce
- 1 tbsp sesame oil
- 1 tbsp olive oil
- 2 cloves garlic, minced
- 1 inch fresh ginger, minced
- 2 cups mixed vegetables (broccoli, bell peppers, snap peas, carrots)
- 1/4 cup sliced green onions
- Cooked brown rice for serving

**Directions:**

1. In a bowl, toss cubed tofu with soy sauce and sesame oil.
2. Heat olive oil in a large skillet or wok over medium-high heat.
3. Add minced garlic and ginger to the skillet and sauté for 1 minute until fragrant.
4. Add marinated tofu to the skillet and cook for 5-7 minutes until golden brown on all sides.
5. Remove tofu from the skillet and set aside.

6. Add mixed vegetables to the skillet and stir-fry for 5-7 minutes until tender-crisp.
7. Return cooked tofu to the skillet and toss to combine with the vegetables.
8. Sprinkle sliced green onions over the stir-fry.
9. Serve vegetable stir-fry over cooked brown rice.
10. Serve hot and enjoy!

**Nutrition Facts (per serving, without rice):**

- Calories: 250
- Protein: 15g
- Fat: 15g
- Carbohydrates: 15g
- Fiber: 5g

# Grilled Chicken Caesar Salad

Prep Time: 15 mins

Total Time: 25 mins

Servings: 2 servings

**Ingredients:**

- 2 boneless, skinless chicken breasts
- 4 cups chopped romaine lettuce
- 1/4 cup grated Parmesan cheese
- 1/4 cup croutons
- 2 tbsp Caesar dressing
- 1 tbsp olive oil
- Salt and pepper to taste
- Optional: lemon wedges for garnish

**Directions:**

1. Preheat grill or grill pan over medium-high heat.
2. Brush chicken breasts with olive oil and season with salt and pepper.
3. Grill chicken for 6-8 minutes per side until cooked through and no longer pink in the center.
4. Remove chicken from the grill and let it rest for 5 minutes before slicing.
5. In a large bowl, toss chopped romaine lettuce with grated Parmesan cheese and croutons.
6. Divide the salad onto serving plates.
7. Top each salad with sliced grilled chicken.
8. Drizzle Caesar dressing over the salads.
9. Garnish with lemon wedges if desired.
10. Serve immediately and enjoy!

**Nutrition Facts (per serving):**

- Calories: 350
- Protein: 30g
- Fat: 15g
- Carbohydrates: 20g
- Fiber: 5g

# Turkey and Veggie Stir-Fry

Prep Time: 15 mins

Total Time: 20 mins

Servings: 4 servings

**Ingredients:**

- 2 tbsp olive oil
- 1 lb ground turkey
- 2 cloves garlic, minced
- 1 inch fresh ginger, minced
- 2 cups mixed vegetables (broccoli, bell peppers, snap peas, carrots)
- 1/4 cup soy sauce
- 1 tbsp honey or maple syrup
- 1 tbsp rice vinegar
- 1 tsp sesame oil
- Cooked brown rice for serving

**Directions:**

1. Heat olive oil in a large skillet or wok over medium-high heat.
2. Add ground turkey to the skillet and cook until browned, breaking it up with a spoon.
3. Add minced garlic and ginger to the skillet and sauté for 1 minute until fragrant.
4. Add mixed vegetables to the skillet and stir-fry for 5-7 minutes until tender-crisp.
5. In a small bowl, whisk together soy sauce, honey or maple syrup, rice vinegar, and sesame oil to make the sauce.
6. Pour the sauce over the turkey and vegetables in the skillet.
7. Stir well to coat everything in the sauce.
8. Continue to cook for another 2-3 minutes until heated through.
9. Serve turkey and veggie stir-fry over cooked brown rice.
10. Serve hot and enjoy!

**Nutrition Facts (per serving, without rice):**

- Calories: 300
- Protein: 25g
- Fat: 15g
- Carbohydrates: 15g
- Fiber: 5g

## Quinoa and Black Bean Salad

Prep Time: 15 mins

Total Time: 25 mins

Servings: 4 servings

**Ingredients:**

- 1 cup quinoa
- 2 cups water or vegetable broth
- 1 can (15 oz) black beans, drained and rinsed
- 1 cup corn kernels (fresh or frozen)
- 1 red bell pepper, diced
- 1/4 cup diced red onion
- 1/4 cup chopped fresh cilantro
- 2 tbsp lime juice
- 2 tbsp olive oil
- 1 tsp ground cumin
- Salt and pepper to taste
- Optional: avocado slices for serving

**Directions:**

1. Rinse quinoa under cold water.
2. In a saucepan, bring water or vegetable broth to a boil.

3. Add quinoa, reduce heat to low, cover, and simmer for 15 minutes until quinoa is cooked and water is absorbed.

4. In a large bowl, combine cooked quinoa, black beans, corn kernels, diced red bell pepper, diced red onion, and chopped fresh cilantro.

5. In a small bowl, whisk together lime juice, olive oil, ground cumin, salt, and pepper to make the dressing.

6. Pour the dressing over the quinoa salad and toss to combine.

7. Serve quinoa and black bean salad with avocado slices if desired.

8. Serve chilled or at room temperature and enjoy!

**Nutrition Facts (per serving):**

- Calories: 350
- Protein: 10g
- Fat: 10g
- Carbohydrates: 55g
- Fiber: 10g

# Miso Glazed Salmon with Steamed Vegetables

Prep Time: 10 mins

Total Time: 20 mins

Servings: 2 servings

**Ingredients:**

- 2 salmon fillets
- 2 tbsp white miso paste
- 1 tbsp honey or maple syrup
- 1 tbsp soy sauce

- 1 tbsp rice vinegar
- 1 tsp sesame oil
- 2 cups mixed vegetables (broccoli, carrots, snap peas)
- Cooked brown rice for serving

**Directions:**

1. Preheat oven to 400°F (200°C).
2. In a small bowl, whisk together white miso paste, honey or maple syrup, soy sauce, rice vinegar, and sesame oil to make the glaze.
3. Place salmon fillets on a baking sheet lined with parchment paper.
4. Brush the miso glaze evenly over the salmon fillets.
5. Bake salmon in the preheated oven for 12-15 minutes until cooked through and flaky.
6. While the salmon is baking, steam mixed vegetables until tender.
7. Serve miso glazed salmon with steamed vegetables and cooked brown rice.
8. Serve hot and enjoy!

**Nutrition Facts (per serving):**

- Calories: 350
- Protein: 25g
- Fat: 15g
- Carbohydrates: 25g
- Fiber: 5g

# Chicken and Vegetable Stir-Fry

Prep Time: 15 mins

Total Time: 25 mins

Servings: 4 servings

**Ingredients:**

- 2 boneless, skinless chicken breasts, thinly sliced
- 2 tbsp soy sauce
- 1 tbsp cornstarch
- 2 tbsp olive oil
- 2 cloves garlic, minced
- 1 inch fresh ginger, minced
- 2 cups mixed vegetables (bell peppers, broccoli, snap peas, carrots)
- 1/4 cup sliced green onions
- Cooked brown rice for serving

**Directions:**

1. In a bowl, toss thinly sliced chicken breasts with soy sauce and cornstarch until evenly coated.
2. Heat olive oil in a large skillet or wok over medium-high heat.
3. Add minced garlic and ginger to the skillet and sauté for 1 minute until fragrant.
4. Add sliced chicken to the skillet and stir-fry for 5-7 minutes until cooked through.
5. Remove cooked chicken from the skillet and set aside.
6. In the same skillet, add mixed vegetables and stir-fry for 5-7 minutes until tender-crisp.

7. Return cooked chicken to the skillet and toss to combine with the vegetables.

8. Sprinkle sliced green onions over the stir-fry.

9. Serve chicken and vegetable stir-fry over cooked brown rice.

10. Serve hot and enjoy!

**Nutrition Facts (per serving, without rice):**

- Calories: 300
- Protein: 25g
- Fat: 15g
- Carbohydrates: 15g
- Fiber: 5g

# Vegetarian Quinoa Bowl

Prep Time: 15 mins

Total Time: 25 mins

Servings: 2 servings

**Ingredients:**

- 1 cup quinoa
- 2 cups water or vegetable broth
- 1 can (15 oz) chickpeas, drained and rinsed
- 1 cup cherry tomatoes, halved
- 1/2 cucumber, diced
- 1/4 cup diced red onion
- 1/4 cup chopped fresh parsley
- 2 tbsp lemon juice
- 2 tbsp olive oil
- Salt and pepper to taste

- Optional: crumbled feta cheese for serving

**Directions:**

1. Rinse quinoa under cold water.

2. In a saucepan, bring water or vegetable broth to a boil.

3. Add quinoa, reduce heat to low, cover, and simmer for 15 minutes until quinoa is cooked and water is absorbed.

4. In a large bowl, combine cooked quinoa, chickpeas, cherry tomatoes, diced cucumber, diced red onion, and chopped fresh parsley.

5. In a small bowl, whisk together lemon juice, olive oil, salt, and pepper to make the dressing.

6. Pour the dressing over the quinoa bowl and toss to combine.

7. Serve quinoa bowl topped with crumbled feta cheese if desired.

8. Serve warm or chilled and enjoy!

**Nutrition Facts (per serving):**

- Calories: 350
- Protein: 12g
- Fat: 12g
- Carbohydrates: 45g
- Fiber: 8g

# Egg Salad Sandwich

Prep Time: 10 mins

Total Time: 15 mins

Servings: 2 sandwiches

**Ingredients:**

- 4 hard-boiled eggs, chopped

- 2 tbsp Greek yogurt
- 1 tbsp Dijon mustard
- 1 tbsp chopped fresh dill
- Salt and pepper to taste
- 4 slices whole grain bread
- 1 cup mixed greens
- Optional: sliced tomatoes and avocado

**Directions:**

1. In a bowl, combine chopped hard-boiled eggs, Greek yogurt, Dijon mustard, chopped fresh dill, salt, and pepper.

2. Spread egg salad mixture evenly onto two slices of whole grain bread.

3. Top each slice with mixed greens, sliced tomatoes, and avocado if desired.

4. Place the remaining slices of bread on top to form sandwiches.

5. Slice sandwiches in half if desired and serve immediately.

**Nutrition Facts (per serving):**

- Calories: 300
- Protein: 15g
- Fat: 12g
- Carbohydrates: 30g
- Fiber: 8g

# Tofu and Vegetable Curry

Prep Time: 15 mins

Total Time: 30 mins

Servings: 4 servings

**Ingredients:**

- 1 block (14 oz) extra-firm tofu, cubed
- 2 tbsp olive oil
- 1 onion, diced
- 2 cloves garlic, minced
- 1 inch fresh ginger, minced
- 2 cups mixed vegetables (bell peppers, carrots, snap peas, cauliflower)
- 1 can (14 oz) coconut milk
- 2 tbsp red curry paste
- 1 tbsp soy sauce
- 1 tbsp maple syrup or honey
- Cooked brown rice for serving

**Directions:**

1. Heat olive oil in a large skillet or pot over medium heat.
2. Add diced onion to the skillet and cook until translucent.
3. Add minced garlic and ginger to the skillet and sauté for 1 minute until fragrant.
4. Add cubed tofu and mixed vegetables to the skillet and cook for 5 minutes.
5. In a bowl, whisk together coconut milk, red curry paste, soy sauce, and maple syrup or honey.
6. Pour the curry sauce over the tofu and vegetables in the skillet.
7. Stir well to combine and bring to a simmer.
8. Simmer for 10-15 minutes until vegetables are tender.
9. Serve tofu and vegetable curry over cooked brown rice.

10. Serve hot and enjoy!

**Nutrition Facts (per serving, without rice):**

- Calories: 350
- Protein: 15g
- Fat: 25g
- Carbohydrates: 20g
- Fiber: 5g

# vegetable Quinoa Salad with Lemon Vinaigrette

Prep Time: 15 mins

Total Time: 25 mins

Servings: 4 servings

**Ingredients:**

- 1 cup quinoa
- 2 cups water or vegetable broth
- 1 cup cherry tomatoes, halved
- 1/2 English cucumber, diced
- 1/4 cup diced red onion
- 1/4 cup chopped fresh parsley
- 2 tbsp lemon juice
- 2 tbsp olive oil
- Salt and pepper to taste
- Optional: crumbled feta cheese for serving

**Directions:**

1. Rinse quinoa under cold water.
2. In a saucepan, bring water or vegetable broth to a boil.

3. Add quinoa, reduce heat to low, cover, and simmer for 15 minutes until quinoa is cooked and water is absorbed.

4. In a large bowl, combine cooked quinoa, cherry tomatoes, diced cucumber, diced red onion, and chopped fresh parsley.

5. In a small bowl, whisk together lemon juice, olive oil, salt, and pepper to make the dressing.

6. Pour the dressing over the quinoa salad and toss to combine.

7. Serve quinoa salad topped with crumbled feta cheese if desired.

8. Serve warm or chilled and enjoy!

**Nutrition Facts (per serving):**

- Calories: 250
- Protein: 6g
- Fat: 10g
- Carbohydrates: 35g
- Fiber: 5g

## Salmon and Asparagus Foil Packets

Prep Time: 10 mins

Total Time: 25 mins

Servings: 2 servings

**Ingredients:**

- 2 salmon fillets
- 1 bunch asparagus, trimmed
- 2 tbsp olive oil
- 2 cloves garlic, minced
- 1 lemon, sliced
- Salt and pepper to taste

- Fresh dill for garnish

**Directions:**

1. Preheat oven to 400°F (200°C).
2. Place each salmon fillet on a large piece of aluminum foil.
3. Arrange trimmed asparagus around the salmon fillets.
4. Drizzle olive oil over the salmon and asparagus.
5. Season with minced garlic, salt, and pepper.
6. Place lemon slices on top of the salmon fillets.
7. Fold the edges of the foil to create a sealed packet.
8. Place foil packets on a baking sheet and bake in the preheated oven for 15 minutes until salmon is cooked through.
9. Carefully open foil packets and transfer salmon and asparagus to serving plates.
10. Garnish with fresh dill and serve hot.

**Nutrition Facts (per serving):**

- Calories: 300
- Protein: 25g
- Fat: 15g
- Carbohydrates: 10g
- Fiber: 5g

## Turkey and Veggie Wrap

Prep Time: 10 mins

Total Time: 15 mins

Servings: 2 servings

**Ingredients:**

- 4 whole grain tortillas

- 1/2 lb deli turkey slices
- 1/2 cup hummus
- 1 cup shredded lettuce
- 1/2 cucumber, sliced
- 1/2 bell pepper, thinly sliced
- 1/4 cup shredded carrots

**Directions:**

1. Lay tortillas flat on a clean surface.
2. Spread hummus evenly over each tortilla.
3. Layer deli turkey slices, shredded lettuce, cucumber slices, bell pepper slices, and shredded carrots on each tortilla.
4. Roll up tortillas tightly to form wraps.
5. Slice wraps in half if desired and serve immediately.

**Nutrition Facts (per serving):**

- Calories: 350
- Protein: 25g
- Fat: 10g
- Carbohydrates: 40g
- Fiber: 8g

# Quinoa Stuffed Bell Peppers

Prep Time: 20 mins

Total Time: 45 mins

Servings: 4 servings

**Ingredients:**

- 4 large bell peppers, halved and seeds removed
- 1 cup quinoa

- 2 cups vegetable broth
- 1 can (15 oz) black beans, drained and rinsed
- 1 cup corn kernels (fresh or frozen)
- 1/2 cup diced tomatoes
- 1/4 cup diced red onion
- 1/4 cup chopped fresh cilantro
- 1 tsp ground cumin
- 1 tsp chili powder
- Salt and pepper to taste
- Optional: shredded cheddar cheese for topping

**Directions:**

1. Preheat oven to 375°F (190°C).
2. In a saucepan, bring vegetable broth to a boil.
3. Add quinoa, reduce heat to low, cover, and simmer for 15 minutes until quinoa is cooked and liquid is absorbed.
4. In a large bowl, combine cooked quinoa, black beans, corn kernels, diced tomatoes, diced red onion, chopped fresh cilantro, ground cumin, chili powder, salt, and pepper.
5. Stuff each halved bell pepper with quinoa mixture.
6. Place stuffed bell peppers in a baking dish.
7. Cover with foil and bake in the preheated oven for 25-30 minutes until peppers are tender.
8. Remove foil, sprinkle shredded cheddar cheese on top if desired, and bake for an additional 5 minutes until cheese is melted.
9. Serve quinoa stuffed bell peppers hot.

**Nutrition Facts (per serving):**

- Calories: 300
- Protein: 10g
- Fat: 5g
- Carbohydrates: 50g
- Fiber: 10g

# Vegetable and Lentil Soup

Prep Time: 15 mins

Total Time: 35 mins

Servings: 4 servings

**Ingredients:**

- 1 tbsp olive oil
- 1 onion, diced
- 2 cloves garlic, minced
- 2 carrots, diced
- 2 celery stalks, diced
- 1 cup dried green lentils, rinsed
- 4 cups vegetable broth
- 1 can (14 oz) diced tomatoes
- 2 cups chopped spinach
- 1 tsp dried thyme
- Salt and pepper to taste

**Directions:**

1. Heat olive oil in a large pot over medium heat.
2. Add diced onion, minced garlic, diced carrots, and diced celery to the pot.

3. Cook for 5 minutes until vegetables are softened.

4. Add dried green lentils, vegetable broth, diced tomatoes, chopped spinach, dried thyme, salt, and pepper to the pot.

5. Bring soup to a boil, then reduce heat to low, cover, and simmer for 20 minutes until lentils are tender.

6. Taste and adjust seasoning if needed.

7. Serve vegetable and lentil soup hot.

**Nutrition Facts (per serving):**

- Calories: 250
- Protein: 15g
- Fat: 5g
- Carbohydrates: 40g
- Fiber: 10g

# Mediterranean Chickpea Salad

- Prep Time: 15 mins
- Total Time: 15 mins
- Servings: 4 servings

**Ingredients:**

- 2 cans (15 oz each) chickpeas, drained and rinsed
- 1 cup cherry tomatoes, halved
- 1 cucumber, diced
- 1/4 cup red onion, finely chopped
- 1/4 cup Kalamata olives, sliced
- 1/4 cup crumbled feta cheese
- 2 tbsp chopped fresh parsley
- 2 tbsp extra virgin olive oil

- 1 tbsp lemon juice
- Salt and pepper to taste

**Directions:**

1. In a large bowl, combine chickpeas, cherry tomatoes, cucumber, red onion, Kalamata olives, crumbled feta cheese, and chopped fresh parsley.
2. Drizzle extra virgin olive oil and lemon juice over the salad.
3. Season with salt and pepper to taste.
4. Toss gently to combine all ingredients.
5. Serve immediately or refrigerate until ready to serve.

**Nutrition Facts (per serving):**

- Calories: 250
- Protein: 10g
- Fat: 10g
- Carbohydrates: 30g
- Fiber: 8g

# Turkey and Avocado Wrap

- Prep Time: 10 mins
- Total Time: 10 mins
- Servings: 2 servings

**Ingredients:**

- 4 whole grain tortillas
- 1/2 lb deli turkey slices
- 1 ripe avocado, sliced
- 1 cup baby spinach leaves
- 1/4 cup hummus

- Salt and pepper to taste

**Directions:**

1. Lay tortillas flat on a clean surface.
2. Spread hummus evenly over each tortilla.
3. Layer deli turkey slices, sliced avocado, and baby spinach leaves on each tortilla.
4. Season with salt and pepper to taste.
5. Roll up tortillas tightly to form wraps.
6. Slice wraps in half if desired and serve immediately.

**Nutrition Facts (per serving):**

- Calories: 300
- Protein: 20g
- Fat: 10g
- Carbohydrates: 30g
- Fiber: 8g

## Quinoa and Black Bean Salad

- Prep Time: 15 mins
- Total Time: 20 mins
- Servings: 4 servings

**Ingredients:**

- 1 cup quinoa, rinsed
- 2 cups water or vegetable broth
- 1 can (15 oz) black beans, drained and rinsed
- 1 red bell pepper, diced
- 1/2 cup corn kernels (fresh or frozen)
- 1/4 cup chopped fresh cilantro

- 2 tbsp lime juice
- 2 tbsp extra virgin olive oil
- Salt and pepper to taste
- Optional: sliced avocado for serving

**Directions:**

1. In a saucepan, bring water or vegetable broth to a boil.
2. Add quinoa, reduce heat to low, cover, and simmer for 15 minutes until quinoa is cooked and liquid is absorbed.
3. In a large bowl, combine cooked quinoa, black beans, diced red bell pepper, corn kernels, and chopped fresh cilantro.
4. In a small bowl, whisk together lime juice, extra virgin olive oil, salt, and pepper to make the dressing.
5. Pour the dressing over the quinoa salad and toss to combine.
6. Serve quinoa and black bean salad with sliced avocado if desired.

**Nutrition Facts (per serving):**

- Calories: 280
- Protein: 10g
- Fat: 8g
- Carbohydrates: 45g
- Fiber: 10g

# Vegetable and Lentil Soup

- Prep Time: 15 mins
- Total Time: 35 mins
- Servings: 4 servings

**Ingredients:**

- 1 tbsp olive oil
- 1 onion, diced
- 2 cloves garlic, minced
- 2 carrots, diced
- 2 celery stalks, diced
- 1 cup dried green lentils, rinsed
- 4 cups vegetable broth
- 1 can (14 oz) diced tomatoes
- 2 cups chopped spinach
- 1 tsp dried thyme
- Salt and pepper to taste

**Directions:**

1. Heat olive oil in a large pot over medium heat.
2. Add diced onion, minced garlic, diced carrots, and diced celery to the pot.
3. Cook for 5 minutes until vegetables are softened.
4. Add dried green lentils, vegetable broth, diced tomatoes, chopped spinach, dried thyme, salt, and pepper to the pot.
5. Bring soup to a boil, then reduce heat to low, cover, and simmer for 20 minutes until lentils are tender.
6. Taste and adjust seasoning if needed.
7. Serve vegetable and lentil soup hot.

**Nutrition Facts (per serving):**

- Calories: 250
- Protein: 15g
- Fat: 5g

- Carbohydrates: 40g
- Fiber: 10g

# Salmon and Quinoa Salad

- Prep Time: 10 mins
- Total Time: 20 mins
- Servings: 2 servings

**Ingredients:**

- 2 salmon fillets
- 1 cup cooked quinoa
- 2 cups mixed salad greens
- 1/2 cup cherry tomatoes, halved
- 1/4 cup diced cucumber
- 1/4 cup sliced red onion
- 2 tbsp chopped fresh dill
- 2 tbsp extra virgin olive oil
- 1 tbsp lemon juice
- Salt and pepper to taste

**Directions:**

1. Season salmon fillets with salt and pepper.
2. Heat olive oil in a skillet over medium-high heat.
3. Add salmon fillets to the skillet and cook for 4-5 minutes on each side until cooked through.
4. In a large bowl, combine cooked quinoa, mixed salad greens, cherry tomatoes, diced cucumber, sliced red onion, and chopped fresh dill.

5. In a small bowl, whisk together extra virgin olive oil, lemon juice, salt, and pepper to make the dressing.

6. Pour the dressing over the salad and toss to combine.

7. Divide the salad mixture onto serving plates and top each with a cooked salmon fillet.

8. Serve immediately and enjoy!

**Nutrition Facts (per serving):**

- Calories: 350
- Protein: 25g
- Fat: 15g
- Carbohydrates: 25g
- Fiber: 5g

# DINNER RECIPES

## Baked Lemon Herb Chicken

Prep Time: 10 mins

Total Time: 35 mins

Servings: 4 servings

**Ingredients:**

- 4 boneless, skinless chicken breasts
- 2 tbsp olive oil
- 2 cloves garlic, minced
- 2 tbsp chopped fresh parsley
- 1 tbsp chopped fresh thyme
- 1 tbsp chopped fresh rosemary
- Zest of 1 lemon
- Juice of 1 lemon
- Salt and pepper to taste

**Directions:**

1. Preheat oven to 400°F (200°C).
2. In a small bowl, whisk together olive oil, minced garlic, chopped fresh parsley, chopped fresh thyme, chopped fresh rosemary, lemon zest, lemon juice, salt, and pepper.
3. Place chicken breasts in a baking dish.
4. Pour the herb and lemon mixture over the chicken breasts, making sure they are evenly coated.
5. Bake in the preheated oven for 25-30 minutes until chicken is cooked through and juices run clear.

6. Serve baked lemon herb chicken hot with your choice of side dishes.

**Nutrition Facts (per serving):**

- Calories: 250
- Protein: 30g
- Fat: 10g
- Carbohydrates: 2g
- Fiber: 1g

# Vegetable Stir-Fry with Tofu

Prep Time: 15 mins

Total Time: 25 mins

Servings: 4 servings

**Ingredients:**

- 1 block (14 oz) firm tofu, pressed and cubed
- 2 tbsp soy sauce
- 1 tbsp sesame oil
- 1 tbsp olive oil
- 2 cloves garlic, minced
- 1 inch ginger, grated
- 1 bell pepper, sliced
- 1 cup broccoli florets
- 1 carrot, julienned
- 1 cup snow peas
- Salt and pepper to taste
- Cooked brown rice or quinoa for serving

**Directions:**

1. In a bowl, toss cubed tofu with soy sauce and sesame oil.
2. Heat olive oil in a large skillet over medium-high heat.
3. Add minced garlic and grated ginger to the skillet and cook for 1 minute until fragrant.
4. Add marinated tofu to the skillet and cook for 5-7 minutes until golden brown.
5. Add sliced bell pepper, broccoli florets, julienned carrot, and snow peas to the skillet.
6. Stir-fry for an additional 5-7 minutes until vegetables are tender-crisp.
7. Season with salt and pepper to taste.
8. Serve vegetable stir-fry with tofu over cooked brown rice or quinoa.

**Nutrition Facts (per serving):**
- Calories: 300
- Protein: 20g
- Fat: 15g
- Carbohydrates: 25g
- Fiber: 6g

# Baked Salmon with Roasted Vegetables

Prep Time: 15 mins

Total Time: 35 mins

Servings: 4 servings

**Ingredients:**
- 4 salmon fillets
- 2 tbsp olive oil

- 1 tsp garlic powder
- 1 tsp dried thyme
- 1 tsp dried rosemary
- 1 tsp paprika
- Salt and pepper to taste
- 2 cups chopped mixed vegetables (e.g., bell peppers, zucchini, cherry tomatoes, red onion)

**Directions:**

1. Preheat oven to 400°F (200°C).
2. Place salmon fillets on a baking sheet lined with parchment paper.
3. In a small bowl, whisk together olive oil, garlic powder, dried thyme, dried rosemary, paprika, salt, and pepper.
4. Brush the herb mixture over the salmon fillets.
5. In a separate bowl, toss chopped mixed vegetables with a drizzle of olive oil, salt, and pepper.
6. Arrange the seasoned vegetables around the salmon fillets on the baking sheet.
7. Bake in the preheated oven for 20-25 minutes until salmon is cooked through and vegetables are roasted.
8. Serve baked salmon with roasted vegetables hot.

**Nutrition Facts (per serving):**

- Calories: 300
- Protein: 25g
- Fat: 15g
- Carbohydrates: 10g

- Fiber: 3g

## Quinoa and Vegetable Stuffed Bell Peppers

Prep Time: 20 mins

Total Time: 50 mins

Servings: 4 servings

**Ingredients:**

- 4 large bell peppers, halved and seeds removed
- 1 cup cooked quinoa
- 1 can (15 oz) black beans, drained and rinsed
- 1 cup corn kernels (fresh or frozen)
- 1/2 cup diced tomatoes
- 1/4 cup diced red onion
- 1/4 cup chopped fresh cilantro
- 1 tsp ground cumin
- 1 tsp chili powder
- Salt and pepper to taste
- Optional: shredded cheddar cheese for topping

**Directions:**

1. Preheat oven to 375°F (190°C).
2. In a large bowl, combine cooked quinoa, black beans, corn kernels, diced tomatoes, diced red onion, chopped fresh cilantro, ground cumin, chili powder, salt, and pepper.
3. Stuff each halved bell pepper with quinoa mixture.
4. Place stuffed bell peppers in a baking dish.
5. Cover with foil and bake in the preheated oven for 25-30 minutes until peppers are tender.

6. Remove foil, sprinkle shredded cheddar cheese on top if desired, and bake for an additional 5 minutes until cheese is melted.

7. Serve quinoa and vegetable stuffed bell peppers hot.

**Nutrition Facts (per serving):**

- Calories: 280
- Protein: 10g
- Fat: 5g
- Carbohydrates: 45g
- Fiber: 10g

# Lemon Garlic Shrimp Pasta

Prep Time: 15 mins

Total Time: 25 mins

Servings: 4 servings

**Ingredients:**

- 8 oz whole wheat spaghetti
- 1 lb. large shrimp, peeled and deveined
- 2 tbsp olive oil
- 4 cloves garlic, minced
- Zest of 1 lemon
- Juice of 1 lemon
- 1/4 cup chopped fresh parsley
- Salt and pepper to taste
- Optional: grated Parmesan cheese for serving

**Directions:**

1. Cook whole wheat spaghetti according to package instructions until al dente. Drain and set aside.
2. In a large skillet, heat olive oil over medium heat.
3. Add minced garlic to the skillet and cook for 1 minute until fragrant.
4. Add shrimp to the skillet and cook for 2-3 minutes on each side until pink and cooked through.
5. Stir in lemon zest, lemon juice, chopped fresh parsley, salt, and pepper.
6. Add cooked whole wheat spaghetti to the skillet and toss to combine with the shrimp and sauce.
7. Serve lemon garlic shrimp pasta hot with grated Parmesan cheese if desired.

**Nutrition Facts (per serving):**

- Calories: 350
- Protein: 25g
- Fat: 10g
- Carbohydrates: 40g
- Fiber: 6g

## Grilled Lemon Herb Chicken

Prep Time: 10 mins

Total Time: 25 mins

Servings: 4 servings

**Ingredients:**

- 4 boneless, skinless chicken breasts
- 2 tbsp olive oil

- 2 cloves garlic, minced
- 2 tbsp chopped fresh parsley
- 1 tbsp chopped fresh thyme
- 1 tbsp chopped fresh rosemary
- Zest of 1 lemon
- Juice of 1 lemon
- Salt and pepper to taste

**Directions:**

1. Preheat grill to medium-high heat.
2. In a small bowl, whisk together olive oil, minced garlic, chopped fresh parsley, chopped fresh thyme, chopped fresh rosemary, lemon zest, lemon juice, salt, and pepper.
3. Place chicken breasts in a shallow dish and pour the marinade over them, turning to coat evenly.
4. Grill chicken breasts for 6-8 minutes on each side until cooked through and grill marks appear.
5. Remove chicken from the grill and let it rest for a few minutes before serving.
6. Serve grilled lemon herb chicken hot with your choice of side dishes.

**Nutrition Facts (per serving):**

- Calories: 250
- Protein: 30g
- Fat: 10g
- Carbohydrates: 2g
- Fiber: 1g

# Vegetable Quinoa Stir-Fry

Prep Time: 15 mins

Total Time: 25 mins

Servings: 4 servings

**Ingredients:**

- 1 cup quinoa, rinsed
- 2 cups water or vegetable broth
- 2 tbsp olive oil
- 2 cloves garlic, minced
- 1 inch ginger, grated
- 2 cups mixed vegetables (e.g., bell peppers, broccoli, carrots, snap peas)
- 1/4 cup soy sauce or tamari
- 1 tbsp rice vinegar
- 1 tbsp sesame oil
- Salt and pepper to taste
- Optional: chopped green onions and sesame seeds for garnish

**Directions:**

1. In a saucepan, bring water or vegetable broth to a boil.
2. Add quinoa, reduce heat to low, cover, and simmer for 15 minutes until quinoa is cooked and liquid is absorbed.
3. In a large skillet or wok, heat olive oil over medium-high heat.
4. Add minced garlic and grated ginger to the skillet and cook for 1 minute until fragrant.
5. Add mixed vegetables to the skillet and stir-fry for 5-7 minutes until vegetables are tender-crisp.

6. Add cooked quinoa to the skillet along with soy sauce or tamari, rice vinegar, sesame oil, salt, and pepper.

7. Stir-fry for an additional 2-3 minutes until quinoa is heated through and flavors are combined.

8. Garnish with chopped green onions and sesame seeds if desired before serving.

**Nutrition Facts (per serving):**

- Calories: 300
- Protein: 10g
- Fat: 15g
- Carbohydrates: 35g
- Fiber: 5g

## Baked Cod with Lemon and Garlic

Prep Time: 10 mins

Total Time: 20 mins

Servings: 4 servings

**Ingredients:**

- 4 cod fillets
- 2 tbsp olive oil
- 2 cloves garlic, minced
- Zest of 1 lemon
- Juice of 1 lemon
- 2 tbsp chopped fresh parsley
- Salt and pepper to taste

**Directions:**

1. Preheat oven to 400°F (200°C).

2. Place cod fillets in a baking dish.

3. In a small bowl, whisk together olive oil, minced garlic, lemon zest, lemon juice, chopped fresh parsley, salt, and pepper.

4. Pour the lemon garlic mixture over the cod fillets, making sure they are evenly coated.

5. Bake in the preheated oven for 12-15 minutes until cod is opaque and flakes easily with a fork.

6. Serve baked cod with lemon and garlic hot with your choice of side dishes.

**Nutrition Facts (per serving):**

- Calories: 200
- Protein: 25g
- Fat: 10g
- Carbohydrates: 2g
- Fiber: 0g

# Vegetable Lentil Soup

Prep Time: 15 mins

Total Time: 40 mins

Servings: 4 servings

**Ingredients:**

- 1 cup dried green lentils, rinsed
- 4 cups vegetable broth
- 1 can (14 oz) diced tomatoes
- 2 carrots, diced
- 2 celery stalks, diced
- 1 onion, diced

- 2 cloves garlic, minced
- 1 tsp dried thyme
- 1 tsp dried rosemary
- Salt and pepper to taste

**Directions:**

1. In a large pot, combine dried green lentils, vegetable broth, diced tomatoes (with juice), diced carrots, diced celery, diced onion, minced garlic, dried thyme, dried rosemary, salt, and pepper.
2. Bring the soup to a boil, then reduce heat to low, cover, and simmer for 25-30 minutes until lentils and vegetables are tender.
3. Adjust seasoning with additional salt and pepper if needed.
4. Serve vegetable lentil soup hot with a slice of whole grain bread or a side salad.

**Nutrition Facts (per serving):**

- Calories: 250
- Protein: 15g
- Fat: 2g
- Carbohydrates: 45g
- Fiber: 15g

## Mediterranean Chickpea Salad

Prep Time: 15 mins

Total Time: 15 mins

Servings: 4 servings

**Ingredients:**

- 2 cans (15 oz each) chickpeas, drained and rinsed
- 1 cucumber, diced
- 1 bell pepper, diced
- 1/2 red onion, finely chopped
- 1 cup cherry tomatoes, halved
- 1/4 cup chopped fresh parsley
- 1/4 cup chopped fresh mint
- 1/4 cup crumbled feta cheese
- 2 tbsp olive oil
- 1 tbsp red wine vinegar
- Salt and pepper to taste
- Optional: olives and lemon wedges for serving

**Directions:**

1. In a large bowl, combine chickpeas, diced cucumber, diced bell pepper, chopped red onion, halved cherry tomatoes, chopped fresh parsley, chopped fresh mint, and crumbled feta cheese.
2. Drizzle olive oil and red wine vinegar over the salad, and toss gently to combine.
3. Season with salt and pepper to taste.
4. Serve Mediterranean chickpea salad at room temperature or chilled, garnished with olives and lemon wedges if desired.

**Nutrition Facts (per serving):**

- Calories: 300
- Protein: 15g
- Fat: 10g
- Carbohydrates: 40g

- Fiber: 10g

## Grilled Salmon with Asparagus

Prep Time: 10 mins

Total Time: 20 mins

Servings: 4 servings

**Ingredients:**

- 4 salmon fillets
- 1 lb asparagus, trimmed
- 2 tbsp olive oil
- 2 cloves garlic, minced
- Zest of 1 lemon
- Juice of 1 lemon
- Salt and pepper to taste

**Directions:**

1. Preheat grill to medium-high heat.
2. Season salmon fillets with salt, pepper, and minced garlic.
3. In a bowl, toss asparagus with olive oil, lemon zest, salt, and pepper.
4. Grill salmon fillets for 4-5 minutes on each side until cooked through and flaky.
5. Grill asparagus for 2-3 minutes, turning occasionally until tender.
6. Remove salmon and asparagus from the grill and drizzle with lemon juice before serving.

**Nutrition Facts (per serving):**

- Calories: 300

- Protein: 25g
- Fat: 20g
- Carbohydrates: 5g
- Fiber: 3g

# Turkey and Vegetable Stir-Fry

Prep Time: 15 mins

Total Time: 25 mins

Servings: 4 servings

**Ingredients:**

- 1 lb turkey breast, sliced
- 2 cups mixed vegetables (e.g., bell peppers, broccoli, carrots, snap peas)
- 2 tbsp olive oil
- 2 cloves garlic, minced
- 2 tbsp soy sauce or tamari
- 1 tbsp rice vinegar
- 1 tsp sesame oil
- Salt and pepper to taste

**Directions:**

1. In a large skillet or wok, heat olive oil over medium-high heat.
2. Add minced garlic to the skillet and cook for 1 minute until fragrant.
3. Add sliced turkey breast to the skillet and cook for 4-5 minutes until browned.
4. Add mixed vegetables to the skillet and stir-fry for 5-7 minutes until vegetables are tender-crisp.

5. In a small bowl, whisk together soy sauce or tamari, rice vinegar, sesame oil, salt, and pepper.

6. Pour the sauce over the turkey and vegetables, and toss to combine.

7. Cook for an additional 2-3 minutes until everything is heated through.

8. Serve turkey and vegetable stir-fry hot with cooked brown rice or quinoa.

**Nutrition Facts (per serving):**

- Calories: 280
- Protein: 30g
- Fat: 10g
- Carbohydrates: 15g
- Fiber: 5g

## Mushroom and Spinach Quinoa Bowl

Prep Time: 10 mins

Total Time: 25 mins

Servings: 4 servings

**Ingredients:**

- 1 cup quinoa, rinsed
- 2 cups vegetable broth
- 1 lb mushrooms, sliced
- 2 cups fresh spinach
- 2 cloves garlic, minced
- 2 tbsp olive oil
- Salt and pepper to taste

- Optional: grated Parmesan cheese for serving

**Directions:**

1. In a saucepan, bring vegetable broth to a boil.
2. Add quinoa, reduce heat to low, cover, and simmer for 15 minutes until quinoa is cooked and liquid is absorbed.
3. In a large skillet, heat olive oil over medium heat.
4. Add minced garlic to the skillet and cook for 1 minute until fragrant.
5. Add sliced mushrooms to the skillet and cook for 5-7 minutes until tender.
6. Add fresh spinach to the skillet and cook for 2-3 minutes until wilted.
7. Season with salt and pepper to taste.
8. Serve mushroom and spinach quinoa bowls hot, topped with grated Parmesan cheese if desired.

**Nutrition Facts (per serving):**

- Calories: 250
- Protein: 10g
- Fat: 10g
- Carbohydrates: 35g
- Fiber: 5g

# Baked Chicken with Roasted Vegetables

Prep Time: 15 mins

Total Time: 35 mins

Servings: 4 servings

**Ingredients:**

- 4 chicken breasts
- 1 lb. mixed vegetables (e.g., carrots, bell peppers, zucchini, cherry tomatoes)
- 2 tbsp olive oil
- 2 cloves garlic, minced
- 1 tsp dried thyme
- 1 tsp dried rosemary
- Salt and pepper to taste

**Directions:**

1. Preheat oven to 400°F (200°C).
2. Place chicken breasts and mixed vegetables on a baking sheet.
3. In a small bowl, whisk together olive oil, minced garlic, dried thyme, dried rosemary, salt, and pepper.
4. Drizzle the olive oil mixture over the chicken and vegetables, and toss to coat evenly.
5. Bake in the preheated oven for 25-30 minutes until chicken is cooked through and vegetables are tender.
6. Serve baked chicken with roasted vegetables hot, garnished with fresh herbs if desired.

**Nutrition Facts (per serving):**

- Calories: 280
- Protein: 30g
- Fat: 10g
- Carbohydrates: 15g
- Fiber: 5g

# Lentil and Vegetable Curry

Prep Time: 15 mins

Total Time: 35 mins

Servings: 4 servings

**Ingredients:**

- 1 cup dried green lentils, rinsed
- 4 cups vegetable broth
- 1 onion, diced
- 2 cloves garlic, minced
- 1 inch ginger, grated
- 2 cups mixed vegetables (e.g., bell peppers, cauliflower, peas, carrots)
- 1 can (14 oz) diced tomatoes
- 2 tbsp curry powder
- 1/2 cup coconut milk
- Salt and pepper to taste
- Optional: chopped fresh cilantro for garnish

**Directions:**

1. In a large pot, combine dried green lentils, vegetable broth, diced onion, minced garlic, grated ginger, mixed vegetables, diced tomatoes (with juice), and curry powder.
2. Bring the curry mixture to a boil, then reduce heat to low, cover, and simmer for 20-25 minutes until lentils and vegetables are tender.
3. Stir in coconut milk and season with salt and pepper to taste.
4. Cook for an additional 5 minutes until heated through.

5. Serve lentil and vegetable curry hot, garnished with chopped fresh cilantro if desired, and accompanied by cooked brown rice or quinoa.

**Nutrition Facts (per serving):**

- Calories: 300
- Protein: 15g
- Fat: 10g
- Carbohydrates: 40g
- Fiber: 10g

## Baked Lemon Herb Chicken

Prep Time: 10 mins

Total Time: 40 mins

Servings: 4 servings

**Ingredients:**

- 4 boneless, skinless chicken breasts
- 2 tbsp olive oil
- 2 cloves garlic, minced
- Zest and juice of 1 lemon
- 1 tsp dried thyme
- 1 tsp dried rosemary
- Salt and pepper to taste
- Fresh parsley for garnish

**Directions:**

1. Preheat oven to 375°F (190°C).
2. In a small bowl, whisk together olive oil, minced garlic, lemon zest, lemon juice, dried thyme, dried rosemary, salt, and pepper.

3. Place chicken breasts in a baking dish and pour the lemon herb marinade over them, ensuring they are evenly coated.
4. Bake in the preheated oven for 30-35 minutes or until chicken is cooked through and juices run clear.
5. Garnish with fresh parsley before serving.

**Nutrition Facts (per serving):**

- Calories: 250
- Protein: 30g
- Fat: 10g
- Carbohydrates: 2g
- Fiber: 0g

# Quinoa Stuffed Bell Peppers

Prep Time: 15 mins

Total Time: 45 mins

Servings: 4 servings

**Ingredients:**

- 4 large bell peppers, halved and seeds removed
- 1 cup quinoa, rinsed
- 2 cups vegetable broth
- 1 can (15 oz) black beans, drained and rinsed
- 1 cup corn kernels
- 1 cup diced tomatoes
- 1 tsp cumin
- 1 tsp paprika
- Salt and pepper to taste
- Optional: shredded cheese for topping

**Directions:**

1. Preheat oven to 375°F (190°C).

2. In a saucepan, bring vegetable broth to a boil and add quinoa. Reduce heat to low, cover, and simmer for 15-20 minutes until quinoa is cooked.

3. In a large bowl, combine cooked quinoa, black beans, corn kernels, diced tomatoes, cumin, paprika, salt, and pepper.

4. Stuff each bell pepper half with the quinoa mixture and place in a baking dish.

5. Cover with foil and bake in the preheated oven for 20-25 minutes until peppers are tender.

6. Remove foil, sprinkle shredded cheese on top (if using), and bake for an additional 5 minutes until cheese is melted and bubbly.

7. Serve quinoa stuffed bell peppers hot.

**Nutrition Facts (per serving):**

- Calories: 300
- Protein: 12g
- Fat: 5g
- Carbohydrates: 55g
- Fiber: 10g

## Salmon and Vegetable Foil Packets

Prep Time: 15 mins

Total Time: 30 mins

Servings: 4 servings

**Ingredients:**

- 4 salmon fillets
- 2 cups mixed vegetables (e.g., zucchini, bell peppers, cherry tomatoes)
- 2 tbsp olive oil
- 2 cloves garlic, minced
- 1 tsp dried oregano
- 1 tsp dried basil
- Salt and pepper to taste
- Lemon wedges for serving

**Directions:**

1. Preheat oven to 400°F (200°C).
2. Cut 4 large pieces of aluminum foil and place a salmon fillet in the center of each.
3. In a bowl, toss mixed vegetables with olive oil, minced garlic, dried oregano, dried basil, salt, and pepper.
4. Divide the vegetable mixture evenly among the foil packets, placing them around the salmon fillets.
5. Fold the edges of the foil to seal the packets tightly.
6. Place the foil packets on a baking sheet and bake in the preheated oven for 15-20 minutes until salmon is cooked through and vegetables are tender.
7. Serve salmon and vegetable foil packets hot with lemon wedges for squeezing over the top.

**Nutrition Facts (per serving):**

- Calories: 320
- Protein: 25g

- Fat: 15g
- Carbohydrates: 15g
- Fiber: 5g

## Vegetarian Lentil Shepherd's Pie

Prep Time: 20 mins

Total Time: 1 hour

Servings: 4 servings

**Ingredients:**

- 2 cups cooked green lentils
- 2 cups mashed sweet potatoes
- 1 onion, diced
- 2 cloves garlic, minced
- 2 carrots, diced
- 1 cup frozen peas
- 1 cup vegetable broth
- 2 tbsp tomato paste
- 1 tsp dried thyme
- 1 tsp dried rosemary
- Salt and pepper to taste

**Directions:**

1. Preheat oven to 375°F (190°C).
2. In a skillet, sauté diced onion and minced garlic in olive oil until translucent.
3. Add diced carrots to the skillet and cook for 5 minutes until slightly softened.

4. Stir in cooked green lentils, frozen peas, vegetable broth, tomato paste, dried thyme, dried rosemary, salt, and pepper. Cook for an additional 5 minutes until heated through.

5. Transfer the lentil mixture to a baking dish and spread mashed sweet potatoes over the top.

6. Bake in the preheated oven for 25-30 minutes until heated through and golden brown on top.

7. Serve vegetarian lentil shepherd's pie hot.

**Nutrition Facts (per serving):**

- Calories: 280
- Protein: 10g
- Fat: 5g
- Carbohydrates: 50g
- Fiber: 10g

# SMOOTHIES RECIPES

## Green Goddess Smoothie

Prep Time: 5 mins

Total Time: 5 mins

Servings: 2 glasses

**Ingredients:**

- 1 cup frozen organic blueberries
- 1/2 cup ice made with filtered or spring water
- 1 cup coconut water
- 1 1/2 cup greens (kale, spinach, or a mix)
- 1/2 avocado
- 1 tbsp. chia seeds
- 1 tsp honey (optional)
- Optional: a scoop of protein powder or collagen powder

**Directions:**

1. In a blender, combine the frozen blueberries, ice, coconut water, greens, avocado, chia seeds, and honey (if using).
2. Blend until smooth, adding more water if needed to reach your desired consistency.
3. Pour into glasses and enjoy immediately.

**Nutritional Information (per serving):**

- Calories: 220
- Protein: 5g
- Fat: 10g
- Carbohydrates: 30g

- Fiber: 10g

## Berry Blast Smoothie

Prep Time: 5 mins

Total Time: 5 mins

Servings: 2 glasses

**Ingredients:**

- 1 cup frozen mixed berries (strawberries, raspberries, blueberries)
- 1/2 cup ice made with filtered or spring water
- 1 cup almond milk
- 1/2 ripe banana
- 1 tbsp. flaxseeds
- 1 tsp honey or maple syrup (optional)

**Directions:**

1. Combine the frozen mixed berries, ice, almond milk, ripe banana, flaxseeds, and honey or maple syrup (if using) in a blender.
2. Blend until smooth and creamy.
3. Pour into glasses and serve immediately.

**Nutritional Information (per serving):**

- Calories: 180
- Protein: 3g
- Fat: 5g
- Carbohydrates: 30g
- Fiber: 8g

# Tropical Sunshine Smoothie

Prep Time: 5 mins

Total Time: 5 mins

Servings: 2 glasses

## Ingredients:

- 1 cup frozen pineapple chunks
- 1/2 cup ice made with filtered or spring water
- 1 cup coconut water
- 1/2 ripe mango, peeled and diced
- 1/2 ripe banana
- 1/4 cup Greek yogurt
- Optional: a handful of spinach for extra greens

## Directions:

1. Place the frozen pineapple chunks, ice, coconut water, ripe mango, banana, and Greek yogurt in a blender.
2. Blend until smooth and creamy.
3. Add spinach if desired and blend again until well combined.
4. Pour into glasses and serve immediately.

## Nutritional Information (per serving):

- Calories: 200
- Protein: 5g
- Fat: 2g
- Carbohydrates: 40g
- Fiber: 6g

# Chocolate Peanut Butter Protein Smoothie

Prep Time: 5 mins

Total Time: 5 mins

Servings: 2 glasses

**Ingredients:**

- 2 ripe bananas
- 1 cup almond milk
- 2 tbsp. peanut butter
- 2 tbsp. cocoa powder
- 1 scoop chocolate protein powder
- 1/2 cup ice made with filtered or spring water
- Optional: a drizzle of honey or maple syrup for sweetness

**Directions:**

1. Add ripe bananas, almond milk, peanut butter, cocoa powder, protein powder, and ice to a blender.
2. Blend until smooth and creamy.
3. If desired, add honey or maple syrup for additional sweetness and blend again.
4. Pour into glasses and enjoy immediately.

**Nutritional Information (per serving):**

- Calories: 280
- Protein: 18g
- Fat: 10g
- Carbohydrates: 35g
- Fiber: 7g

# Detox Green Smoothie

Prep Time: 5 mins

Total Time: 5 mins

Servings: 2 glasses

**Ingredients:**

- 1 cup spinach
- 1/2 cup kale
- 1/2 cucumber, peeled and chopped
- 1 green apple, cored and chopped
- 1/2 lemon, juiced
- 1 cup coconut water
- 1/2 cup ice made with filtered or spring water
- Optional: a knob of ginger for added flavor

**Directions:**

1. Combine spinach, kale, cucumber, green apple, lemon juice, coconut water, ice, and ginger (if using) in a blender.
2. Blend until smooth and creamy.
3. Pour into glasses and serve immediately.

**Nutritional Information (per serving):**

- Calories: 100
- Protein: 3g
- Fat: 1g
- Carbohydrates: 25g
- Fiber: 7g

## Berry Protein Smoothie

Prep Time: 5 mins

Total Time: 5 mins

Servings: 2 glasses

**Ingredients:**

- 1 cup frozen mixed berries (strawberries, blueberries, raspberries)
- 1/2 cup almond milk
- 1/2 cup Greek yogurt
- 1 scoop vanilla protein powder
- 1 tbsp chia seeds
- 1/2 banana
- 1/2 cup ice made with filtered or spring water

**Directions:**

1. Combine frozen mixed berries, almond milk, Greek yogurt, protein powder, chia seeds, banana, and ice in a blender.
2. Blend until smooth and creamy.
3. If the smoothie is too thick, add more water to achieve the desired consistency.
4. Pour into glasses and serve immediately.

**Nutritional Information (per serving):**

- Calories: 250
- Protein: 25g
- Fat: 6g
- Carbohydrates: 25g
- Fiber: 8g

# Pineapple Coconut Smoothie

Prep Time: 5 mins

Total Time: 5 mins

Servings: 2 glasses

**Ingredients:**

- 1 cup frozen pineapple chunks
- 1/2 cup coconut milk
- 1/2 cup Greek yogurt
- 1/2 banana
- 1 tbsp shredded coconut
- 1/2 cup ice made with filtered or spring water

**Directions:**

1. In a blender, combine frozen pineapple chunks, coconut milk, Greek yogurt, banana, shredded coconut, and ice.
2. Blend until smooth and creamy.
3. Add more water if needed for desired consistency.
4. Pour into glasses and serve immediately.

**Nutritional Information (per serving):**

- Calories: 220
- Protein: 7g
- Fat: 10g
- Carbohydrates: 30g
- Fiber: 6g

## Mango Avocado Smoothie

Prep Time: 5 mins

Total Time: 5 mins

Servings: 2 glasses

**Ingredients:**

- 1 cup frozen mango chunks
- 1/2 avocado
- 1/2 cup almond milk

- 1/2 cup Greek yogurt
- 1 tbsp honey
- 1/2 cup ice made with filtered or spring water

**Directions:**

1. In a blender, combine frozen mango chunks, avocado, almond milk, Greek yogurt, honey, and ice.
2. Blend until smooth and creamy.
3. Adjust consistency with more water if necessary.
4. Pour into glasses and serve immediately.

**Nutritional Information (per serving):**

- Calories: 240
- Protein: 8g
- Fat: 8g
- Carbohydrates: 35g
- Fiber: 6g

# Green Tea Smoothie

Prep Time: 5 mins

Total Time: 5 mins

Servings: 2 glasses

**Ingredients:**

- 1 cup brewed green tea, cooled
- 1/2 cup frozen pineapple chunks
- 1/2 cup spinach
- 1/2 banana
- 1/2 cup Greek yogurt
- 1 tbsp honey

- 1/2 cup ice made with filtered or spring water

**Directions:**

1. Brew green tea and let it cool.
2. In a blender, combine cooled green tea, frozen pineapple chunks, spinach, banana, Greek yogurt, honey, and ice.
3. Blend until smooth and creamy.
4. Adjust consistency with more water if needed.
5. Pour into glasses and serve immediately.

**Nutritional Information (per serving):**

- Calories: 210
- Protein: 7g
- Fat: 2g
- Carbohydrates: 40g
- Fiber: 5g

## Chocolate Banana Peanut Butter Smoothie

Prep Time: 5 mins

Total Time: 5 mins

Servings: 2 glasses

**Ingredients:**

- 1 cup almond milk
- 1 banana
- 2 tbsp cocoa powder
- 2 tbsp peanut butter
- 1 scoop chocolate protein powder
- 1/2 cup ice made with filtered or spring water

**Directions:**

1. In a blender, combine almond milk, banana, cocoa powder, peanut butter, protein powder, and ice.
2. Blend until smooth and creamy.
3. Adjust consistency with more water if necessary.
4. Pour into glasses and serve immediately.

**Nutritional Information (per serving):**

- Calories: 280
- Protein: 18g
- Fat: 10g
- Carbohydrates: 30g
- Fiber: 8g

# Green Detox Smoothie

Prep Time: 5 mins

Total Time: 5 mins

Servings: 2 glasses

**Ingredients:**

- 1 cup spinach
- 1/2 cucumber, peeled and chopped
- 1/2 green apple, cored and chopped
- 1/2 avocado
- 1/2 lemon, juiced
- 1/2 cup coconut water
- 1/2 cup ice made with filtered or spring water
- Optional: 1 tsp honey or sweetener of choice

**Directions:**

1. Combine spinach, cucumber, green apple, avocado, lemon juice, coconut water, and ice in a blender.
2. Blend until smooth and creamy.
3. Taste and add honey or sweetener if desired.
4. Pour into glasses and serve immediately.

**Nutritional Information (per serving):**

- Calories: 120
- Protein: 3g
- Fat: 7g
- Carbohydrates: 14g
- Fiber: 6g

# Berry Blast Smoothie

Prep Time: 5 mins

Total Time: 5 mins

Servings: 2 glasses

**Ingredients:**

- 1 cup mixed berries (strawberries, blueberries, raspberries)
- 1/2 banana
- 1/2 cup Greek yogurt
- 1/2 cup almond milk
- 1 tbsp chia seeds
- 1/2 cup ice made with filtered or spring water

**Directions:**

1. Place mixed berries, banana, Greek yogurt, almond milk, chia seeds, and ice in a blender.
2. Blend until smooth.

3. Add more water if needed to reach desired consistency.

4. Pour into glasses and serve immediately.

**Nutritional Information (per serving):**

- Calories: 160
- Protein: 7g
- Fat: 4g
- Carbohydrates: 24g
- Fiber: 8g

# Tropical Paradise Smoothie

Prep Time: 5 mins

Total Time: 5 mins

Servings: 2 glasses

**Ingredients:**

- 1/2 cup pineapple chunks
- 1/2 cup mango chunks
- 1/2 banana
- 1/2 cup coconut milk
- 1/2 cup ice made with filtered or spring water
- Optional: 1 tbsp shredded coconut

**Directions:**

1. Combine pineapple chunks, mango chunks, banana, coconut milk, and ice in a blender.

2. Blend until smooth.

3. Add shredded coconut if desired and blend briefly.

4. Pour into glasses and serve immediately.

**Nutritional Information (per serving):**

- Calories: 180
- Protein: 2g
- Fat: 8g
- Carbohydrates: 30g
- Fiber: 5g

## Creamy Peanut Butter Smoothie

- **Prep Time:** 5 mins
- **Total Time:** 5 mins
- **Servings:** 2 glasses

**Ingredients:**

- 2 tbsp natural peanut butter
- 1 banana
- 1 cup spinach
- 1/2 cup Greek yogurt
- 1/2 cup almond milk
- 1/2 cup ice made with filtered or spring water

**Directions:**

1. In a blender, combine peanut butter, banana, spinach, Greek yogurt, almond milk, and ice.
2. Blend until smooth.
3. Adjust thickness with more water if needed.
4. Pour into glasses and serve immediately.

**Nutritional Information (per serving):**

- Calories: 240
- Protein: 10g
- Fat: 14g

- Carbohydrates: 21g
- Fiber: 5g

# Chia Berry Smoothie Bowl

Prep Time: 5 mins

Total Time: 5 mins

Servings: 2 bowls

**Ingredients:**

- 1 cup mixed berries (strawberries, blueberries, raspberries)
- 1/2 banana
- 1/2 cup Greek yogurt
- 2 tbsp chia seeds
- 1/2 cup almond milk
- Toppings: sliced banana, granola, shredded coconut (optional)

**Directions:**

1. Blend mixed berries, banana, Greek yogurt, chia seeds, and almond milk until smooth.
2. Pour into bowls.
3. Top with sliced banana, granola, and shredded coconut if desired.
4. Serve immediately.

**Nutritional Information (per serving):**

- Calories: 180
- Protein: 8g
- Fat: 5g
- Carbohydrates: 25g
- Fiber: 9g

**Protein-Packed Berry Blast Smoothie**

Prep Time: 5 mins

Total Time: 5 mins

Servings: 2 glasses

**Ingredients:**

- 1 cup mixed berries (strawberries, blueberries, raspberries)
- 1/2 banana
- 1/2 cup Greek yogurt
- 1 scoop protein powder (whey or plant-based)
- 1/2 cup almond milk
- 1 tbsp chia seeds
- 1/2 cup ice made with filtered or spring water

**Directions:**

1. Combine mixed berries, banana, Greek yogurt, protein powder, almond milk, chia seeds, and ice in a blender.
2. Blend until smooth and creamy.
3. Adjust consistency by adding more water if needed.
4. Pour into glasses and serve immediately.

**Nutritional Information (per serving):**

- Calories: 250
- Protein: 20g
- Fat: 7g
- Carbohydrates: 30g
- Fiber: 8g

# Green Power Smoothie

Prep Time: 5 mins

Total Time: 5 mins

Servings: 2 glasses

**Ingredients:**

- 2 cups spinach
- 1/2 cucumber, peeled and chopped
- 1/2 avocado
- 1/2 cup coconut water
- 1/2 cup pineapple chunks
- 1/2 lime, juiced
- 1/2 cup ice made with filtered or spring water

**Directions:**

1. Blend spinach, cucumber, avocado, coconut water, pineapple chunks, lime juice, and ice until smooth.
2. Adjust consistency with additional water if necessary.
3. Pour into glasses and serve immediately.

**Nutritional Information (per serving):**

- Calories: 180
- Protein: 4g
- Fat: 10g
- Carbohydrates: 22g
- Fiber: 8g

## Creamy Peanut Butter Banana Smoothie

Prep Time: 5 mins

Total Time: 5 mins

Servings: 2 glasses

**Ingredients:**

- 2 tbsp natural peanut butter
- 1 banana
- 1/2 cup Greek yogurt
- 1/2 cup almond milk
- 1/2 cup ice made with filtered or spring water

**Directions:**

1. In a blender, combine peanut butter, banana, Greek yogurt, almond milk, and ice.
2. Blend until smooth and creamy.
3. Add more water if needed to reach desired consistency.
4. Pour into glasses and serve immediately.

**Nutritional Information (per serving):**

- Calories: 280
- Protein: 14g
- Fat: 15g
- Carbohydrates: 25g
- Fiber: 5g

## Turmeric Mango Smoothie

Prep Time: 5 mins

Total Time: 5 mins

Servings: 2 glasses

**Ingredients:**

- 1 cup frozen mango chunks
- 1/2 banana
- 1/2 cup Greek yogurt
- 1/2 tsp ground turmeric

- 1/2 tsp ground ginger
- 1/2 cup almond milk
- 1/2 cup ice made with filtered or spring water

**Directions:**

1. Blend mango chunks, banana, Greek yogurt, turmeric, ginger, almond milk, and ice until smooth.
2. Adjust thickness with additional water if desired.
3. Pour into glasses and serve immediately.

**Nutritional Information (per serving):**

- Calories: 160
- Protein: 7g
- Fat: 3g
- Carbohydrates: 28g
- Fiber: 4g

# Antioxidant Superfood Smoothie

Prep Time: 5 mins

Total Time: 5 mins

Servings: 2 glasses

**Ingredients:**

- 1 cup mixed berries (strawberries, blueberries, raspberries)
- 1/2 cup spinach
- 1/2 cup kale
- 1/2 cup Greek yogurt
- 1/2 cup almond milk
- 1 tbsp honey
- 1/2 cup ice made with filtered or spring water

**Directions:**

1. Blend mixed berries, spinach, kale, Greek yogurt, almond milk, honey, and ice until smooth.

2. Adjust sweetness with more honey if desired.

3. Pour into glasses and serve immediately.

**Nutritional Information (per serving):**

- Calories: 180
- Protein: 8g
- Fat: 3g
- Carbohydrates: 30g
- Fiber: 7g

# SNACKS RECIPES

## Chia Seed Pudding

Prep Time: 5 mins

Total Time: 4 hours (chilling time)

Servings: 2 servings

**Ingredients:**

- 1/4 cup chia seeds
- 1 cup almond milk (or dairy-free alternative)
- 1 tablespoon maple syrup or honey (optional)
- 1/2 teaspoon vanilla extract
- Fresh fruit for topping (e.g., berries, sliced banana)

**Directions:**

1. In a mixing bowl, combine chia seeds, almond milk, maple syrup or honey (if using), and vanilla extract. Stir well to combine.
2. Cover the bowl and refrigerate for at least 4 hours or overnight, until the mixture has thickened to a pudding-like consistency.
3. Before serving, stir the chia pudding to redistribute the seeds. Divide the pudding between two serving glasses or bowls.
4. Top each serving with fresh fruit.
5. Serve chilled and enjoy!

**Nutrition Facts (per serving):**

- Calories: 150
- Protein: 5g
- Fat: 8g

- Carbohydrates: 16g
- Fiber: 10g

## Apple and Peanut Butter Slices

Prep Time: 5 mins

Total Time: 5 mins

Servings: 2 servings

**Ingredients:**

- 1 apple, sliced
- 2 tablespoons peanut butter (or almond butter)
- 1 tablespoon honey (optional)
- 1 tablespoon chopped nuts (e.g., almonds, walnuts)

**Directions:**

1. Arrange the apple slices on a plate or serving dish.
2. Spread peanut butter over each apple slice.
3. Drizzle with honey (if using) and sprinkle with chopped nuts.
4. Serve immediately and enjoy!

**Nutrition Facts (per serving):**

- Calories: 200
- Protein: 5g
- Fat: 12g
- Carbohydrates: 20g
- Fiber: 4g

## Greek Yogurt with Berries and Honey

Prep Time: 5 mins

Total Time: 5 mins

Servings: 2 servings

**Ingredients:**

- 1 cup plain Greek yogurt
- 1/2 cup mixed berries (e.g., strawberries, blueberries, raspberries)
- 2 tablespoons honey
- 2 tablespoons granola (optional)

**Directions:**

1. Divide the Greek yogurt between two serving bowls.
2. Top each bowl with mixed berries.
3. Drizzle honey over the berries.
4. Optionally, sprinkle granola over the top for added crunch.
5. Serve immediately and enjoy!

**Nutrition Facts (per serving):**

- Calories: 200
- Protein: 15g
- Fat: 4g
- Carbohydrates: 30g
- Fiber: 2g

## Vegetable Sticks with Hummus

Prep Time: 10 mins

Total Time: 10 mins

Servings: 2 servings

**Ingredients:**

- Assorted vegetable sticks (e.g., carrots, cucumbers, bell peppers)
- 1/2 cup hummus

**Directions:**

1. Wash and cut assorted vegetables into sticks.
2. Arrange the vegetable sticks on a serving plate.
3. Serve with hummus for dipping.
4. Enjoy this crunchy and satisfying snack!

**Nutrition Facts (per serving):**

- Calories: 150
- Protein: 5g
- Fat: 8g
- Carbohydrates: 15g
- Fiber: 6g

# Trail Mix

Prep Time: 5 mins

Total Time: 5 mins

Servings: 2 servings

**Ingredients:**

- 1/4 cup almonds
- 1/4 cup cashews
- 1/4 cup dried cranberries
- 1/4 cup pumpkin seeds
- 1/4 cup dark chocolate chips

**Directions:**

1. In a mixing bowl, combine all the ingredients.

2. Toss well to mix.

3. Divide the trail mix between two small resalable bags for easy portioning.

4. Enjoy as a convenient and nutritious snack on-the-go!

**Nutrition Facts (per serving):**

- Calories: 250
- Protein: 8g
- Fat: 15g
- Carbohydrates: 25g
- Fiber: 4g

# Energy Balls

Prep Time: 15 mins

Total Time: 15 mins

Servings: 12 balls

**Ingredients:**

- 1 cup rolled oats
- 1/2 cup almond butter
- 1/4 cup honey or maple syrup
- 1/4 cup ground flaxseed
- 1/4 cup chopped nuts (e.g., almonds, walnuts)
- 1/4 cup dried cranberries or raisins
- 1 teaspoon vanilla extract
- Pinch of salt
- Optional: shredded coconut, cocoa powder for coating

**Directions:**

1. In a mixing bowl, combine rolled oats, almond butter, honey or maple syrup, ground flaxseed, chopped nuts, dried cranberries or raisins, vanilla extract, and a pinch of salt.
2. Stir well until all ingredients are evenly incorporated.
3. Scoop out tablespoon-sized portions of the mixture and roll into balls using your hands.
4. If desired, roll the energy balls in shredded coconut or cocoa powder for extra flavor.
5. Place the energy balls on a baking sheet lined with parchment paper and chill in the refrigerator for at least 30 minutes before serving.
6. Store leftovers in an airtight container in the refrigerator for up to one week.

**Nutrition Facts (per serving - 1 ball):**

- Calories: 120
- Protein: 3g
- Fat: 7g
- Carbohydrates: 12g
- Fiber: 2g

## Vegetable Sushi Rolls

Prep Time: 20 mins

Total Time: 20 mins

Servings: 4 rolls

**Ingredients:**

- 4 nori seaweed sheets
- 2 cups cooked quinoa

- 1 small cucumber, julienned
- 1 carrot, julienned
- 1 avocado, sliced
- 1/4 cup pickled ginger (optional)
- 1/4 cup low-sodium soy sauce or tamari
- Wasabi and/or sesame seeds for garnish

**Directions:**

1. Place a nori seaweed sheet shiny side down on a sushi rolling mat or clean kitchen towel.
2. Spread a thin layer of cooked quinoa evenly over the nori sheet, leaving a 1-inch border at the top edge.
3. Arrange julienned cucumber, carrot, avocado, and pickled ginger in a line across the center of the quinoa.
4. Using the sushi rolling mat or kitchen towel, tightly roll the nori sheet away from you, pressing gently as you roll to seal the ingredients.
5. Use a sharp knife to slice the sushi roll into 6-8 pieces.
6. Serve with low-sodium soy sauce or tamari for dipping, and garnish with wasabi and sesame seeds if desired.
7. Enjoy these nutritious vegetable sushi rolls as a satisfying snack!

**Nutrition Facts (per serving - 1 roll):**

- Calories: 180
- Protein: 5g
- Fat: 6g
- Carbohydrates: 28g

- Fiber: 6g

## Roasted Chickpeas

Prep Time: 5 mins

Total Time: 40 mins

Servings: 4 servings

**Ingredients:**

- 2 cans (15 ounces each) chickpeas, drained and rinsed
- 2 tablespoons olive oil
- 1 teaspoon ground cumin
- 1 teaspoon paprika
- 1/2 teaspoon garlic powder
- 1/2 teaspoon salt

**Directions:**

1. Preheat your oven to 400°F (200°C). Line a baking sheet with parchment paper.
2. Pat the rinsed chickpeas dry with a clean kitchen towel or paper towels to remove excess moisture.
3. In a mixing bowl, toss the dried chickpeas with olive oil, ground cumin, paprika, garlic powder, and salt until evenly coated.
4. Spread the seasoned chickpeas in a single layer on the prepared baking sheet.
5. Roast in the preheated oven for 30-40 minutes, stirring halfway through, until the chickpeas are golden brown and crispy.
6. Remove from the oven and let cool before serving.

7. Enjoy these crunchy roasted chickpeas as a nutritious and satisfying snack!

**Nutrition Facts (per serving):**

- Calories: 220
- Protein: 8g
- Fat: 8g
- Carbohydrates: 28g
- Fiber: 7g

# Caprese Skewers

Prep Time: 15 mins

Total Time: 15 mins

Servings: 4 skewers

**Ingredients:**

- 8 cherry tomatoes
- 8 small fresh mozzarella balls (bocconcini)
- 8 fresh basil leaves
- 1 tablespoon balsamic glaze
- Salt and pepper to taste

**Directions:**

1. Thread a cherry tomato, a fresh mozzarella ball, and a basil leaf onto each skewer.
2. Repeat until all ingredients are used, making 4 skewers in total.
3. Arrange the skewers on a serving platter.
4. Drizzle balsamic glaze over the skewers and season with salt and pepper to taste.
5. Serve immediately and enjoy this classic Italian-inspired snack!

**Nutrition Facts (per serving - 2 skewers):**

- Calories: 120
- Protein: 8g
- Fat: 8g
- Carbohydrates: 4g
- Fiber: 1g

# Hummus Stuffed Bell Peppers

Prep Time: 10 mins

Total Time: 10 mins

Servings: 4 servings

**Ingredients:**

- 2 large bell peppers, halved and seeds removed
- 1 cup hummus (store-bought or homemade)
- Paprika and fresh parsley for garnish

**Directions:**

1. Fill each bell pepper half with a generous scoop of hummus.
2. Sprinkle paprika over the top of the hummus for added flavor and color.
3. Garnish with fresh parsley for a pop of freshness.
4. Serve immediately, or store in the refrigerator until ready to enjoy.
5. These hummus-stuffed bell peppers make a nutritious and satisfying snack option!

**Nutrition Facts (per serving - 1 stuffed pepper half):**

- Calories: 100
- Protein: 4g

- Fat: 6g
- Carbohydrates: 10g
- Fiber: 4g

## Quinoa Salad with Avocado and Chickpeas

Prep Time: 15 mins

Total Time: 20 mins

Servings: 4 servings

**Ingredients:**

- 1 cup cooked quinoa
- 1 avocado, diced
- 1 can (15 ounces) chickpeas, drained and rinsed
- 1 cup cherry tomatoes, halved
- 1/4 cup chopped fresh cilantro or parsley
- 2 tablespoons olive oil
- 1 tablespoon lemon juice
- Salt and pepper to taste

**Directions:**

1. In a large mixing bowl, combine cooked quinoa, diced avocado, chickpeas, cherry tomatoes, and chopped cilantro or parsley.
2. Drizzle olive oil and lemon juice over the salad ingredients.
3. Season with salt and pepper to taste.
4. Toss well to combine all the ingredients evenly.
5. Serve immediately or refrigerate until ready to enjoy.
6. This quinoa salad with avocado and chickpeas makes a delicious and satisfying snack option!

**Nutrition Facts (per serving):**

- Calories: 280
- Protein: 9g
- Fat: 14g
- Carbohydrates: 31g
- Fiber: 9g

## Turkey and Cheese Roll-Ups

Prep Time: 10 mins

Total Time: 10 mins

Servings: 2 servings

**Ingredients:**

- 4 slices turkey breast
- 2 slices cheese (e.g., cheddar, Swiss)
- 1/2 avocado, sliced
- 1/2 cup baby spinach leaves
- Mustard or mayonnaise for spreading (optional)

**Directions:**

1. Lay the turkey slices flat on a clean work surface.
2. Place a slice of cheese on each turkey slice.
3. Top each slice with avocado slices and baby spinach leaves.
4. If desired, spread mustard or mayonnaise over the ingredients.
5. Roll up each turkey slice tightly to create a roll-up.
6. Secure with toothpicks if necessary.
7. Slice each roll-up into bite-sized pieces.
8. Serve immediately or pack for a convenient snack on-the-go.

**Nutrition Facts (per serving):**

- Calories: 250

- Protein: 20g
- Fat: 16g
- Carbohydrates: 7g
- Fiber: 4g

## Greek Yogurt Parfait

Prep Time: 5 mins

Total Time: 5 mins

Servings: 2 servings

**Ingredients:**

- 1 cup plain Greek yogurt
- 1/2 cup mixed berries (e.g., strawberries, blueberries, raspberries)
- 1/4 cup granola
- 2 tablespoons honey or maple syrup (optional)

**Directions:**

1. In two serving glasses or bowls, layer plain Greek yogurt, mixed berries, and granola.
2. Drizzle honey or maple syrup over the top if desired.
3. Repeat the layers until all ingredients are used.
4. Serve immediately and enjoy this nutritious and delicious Greek yogurt parfait!

**Nutrition Facts (per serving):**

- Calories: 250
- Protein: 18g
- Fat: 6g
- Carbohydrates: 35g

- Fiber: 5g

## Zucchini and Carrot Fritters

Prep Time: 15 mins

Total Time: 25 mins

Servings: 4 servings

**Ingredients:**

- 1 medium zucchini, grated
- 1 medium carrot, grated
- 2 eggs
- 1/4 cup whole wheat flour or almond flour
- 2 tablespoons grated Parmesan cheese
- 2 tablespoons chopped fresh parsley or cilantro
- Salt and pepper to taste
- Olive oil for cooking

**Directions:**

1. In a large mixing bowl, combine grated zucchini, grated carrot, eggs, whole wheat flour or almond flour, grated Parmesan cheese, chopped fresh parsley or cilantro, salt, and pepper.
2. Stir well until all ingredients are evenly combined.
3. Heat olive oil in a non-stick skillet over medium heat.
4. Scoop out tablespoon-sized portions of the fritter mixture and drop onto the skillet.
5. Flatten each portion with a spatula to form a fritter.
6. Cook for 3-4 minutes on each side, or until golden brown and cooked through.
7. Remove from the skillet and drain on paper towels.

8. Serve the zucchini and carrot fritters warm or at room temperature.

9. These fritters can be enjoyed on their own or served with a dollop of Greek yogurt or hummus for dipping.

**Nutrition Facts (per serving):**

- Calories: 150
- Protein: 7g
- Fat: 8g
- Carbohydrates: 12g
- Fiber: 3g

# Edamame and Avocado Dip

Prep Time: 10 mins

Total Time: 10 mins

Servings: 4 servings

**Ingredients:**

- 1 cup shelled edamame, cooked
- 1 ripe avocado
- 1 garlic clove, minced
- 2 tablespoons lemon juice
- 2 tablespoons chopped fresh cilantro
- Salt and pepper to taste
- Optional: red pepper flakes for a spicy kick

**Directions:**

1. In a food processor or blender, combine cooked edamame, ripe avocado, minced garlic, lemon juice, chopped fresh cilantro, salt, and pepper.

2. Blend until smooth and creamy, scraping down the sides of the bowl as needed.
3. Taste and adjust seasoning as desired, adding red pepper flakes for a spicy kick if desired.
4. Transfer the dip to a serving bowl.
5. Serve with raw vegetable sticks (e.g., carrots, celery, bell peppers) or whole grain crackers for dipping.
6. Enjoy this nutritious and flavorful edamame and avocado dip as a satisfying snack option!

**Nutrition Facts (per serving):**

- Calories: 150
- Protein: 7g
- Fat: 9g
- Carbohydrates: 12g
- Fiber: 7g

# Hummus and Veggie Wraps

Prep Time: 10 mins

Total Time: 10 mins

Servings: 2 wraps

**Ingredients:**

- 2 whole grain tortillas
- 1/2 cup hummus (store-bought or homemade)
- 1 cup mixed vegetables (e.g., shredded carrots, sliced cucumber, bell pepper strips)
- Handful of fresh spinach leaves

**Directions:**

1. Spread a generous layer of hummus onto each tortilla.
2. Arrange mixed vegetables and spinach leaves evenly over the hummus.
3. Roll up the tortillas tightly, enclosing the filling.
4. Slice each wrap in half diagonally.
5. Serve immediately, or wrap in parchment paper for a convenient on-the-go snack.

**Nutrition Facts (per serving - 1 wrap):**

- Calories: 200
- Protein: 7g
- Fat: 8g
- Carbohydrates: 28g
- Fiber: 6g

# Banana and Almond Butter Bites

Prep Time: 5 mins

Total Time: 5 mins

Servings: 2 servings

**Ingredients:**

- 1 large banana, sliced
- 2 tablespoons almond butter (or peanut butter)
- Optional toppings: shredded coconut, dark chocolate chips, chopped nuts

**Directions:**

1. Spread almond butter onto banana slices.
2. Sprinkle with optional toppings like shredded coconut, dark chocolate chips, or chopped nuts.

3. Enjoy immediately as a delicious and nutritious snack!

**Nutrition Facts (per serving):**

- Calories: 180
- Protein: 4g
- Fat: 11g
- Carbohydrates: 20g
- Fiber: 3g

## Greek Yogurt with Honey and Walnuts

Prep Time: 5 mins

Total Time: 5 mins

Servings: 2 servings

**Ingredients:**

- 1 cup plain Greek yogurt
- 2 tablespoons honey
- 1/4 cup chopped walnuts

**Directions:**

1. Divide Greek yogurt between two serving bowls.
2. Drizzle honey over each serving.
3. Sprinkle chopped walnuts over the top.
4. Serve immediately and enjoy this creamy and satisfying snack!

**Nutrition Facts (per serving):**

- Calories: 250
- Protein: 15g
- Fat: 12g
- Carbohydrates: 20g
- Fiber: 2g

# Cottage Cheese with Pineapple

Prep Time: 5 mins

Total Time: 5 mins

Servings: 2 servings

**Ingredients:**

- 1 cup cottage cheese
- 1/2 cup diced pineapple

**Directions:**

1. Divide cottage cheese between two serving bowls.
2. Top each serving with diced pineapple.
3. Serve immediately or refrigerate until ready to enjoy.
4. This cottage cheese and pineapple combination provides a balance of protein and natural sweetness, making it a satisfying snack option!

**Nutrition Facts (per serving):**

- Calories: 150
- Protein: 14g
- Fat: 3g
- Carbohydrates: 18g
- Fiber: 2g

# Roasted Edamame

Prep Time: 5 mins

Total Time: 20 mins

Servings: 2 servings

**Ingredients:**

- 1 cup frozen edamame, thawed

- 1 tablespoon olive oil
- 1/2 teaspoon garlic powder
- 1/2 teaspoon smoked paprika
- Salt to taste

**Directions:**

1. Preheat oven to 400°F (200°C). Line a baking sheet with parchment paper.
2. In a mixing bowl, toss thawed edamame with olive oil, garlic powder, smoked paprika, and salt until evenly coated.
3. Spread seasoned edamame in a single layer on the prepared baking sheet.
4. Roast in the preheated oven for 15-20 minutes, stirring halfway through, until golden brown and crispy.
5. Remove from the oven and let cool slightly before serving.
6. Enjoy these roasted edamame as a crunchy and flavorful snack option!

**Nutrition Facts (per serving):**

- Calories: 150
- Protein: 12g
- Fat: 7g
- Carbohydrates: 10g
- Fiber: 6g

# DESSERTS RECIPES

## Fruit Salad with Honcy Lime Dressing

Prep Time: 15 mins

Total Time: 15 mins

Servings: 4 servings

**Ingredients:**

- 2 cups mixed fruits (e.g., strawberries, blueberries, kiwi, pineapple, grapes)
- 1 tablespoon honey
- 1 tablespoon lime juice
- 1 teaspoon lime zest
- Fresh mint leaves for garnish (optional)

**Directions:**

1. Wash and prepare the fruits as needed, then chop them into bite-sized pieces.
2. In a small bowl, whisk together honey, lime juice, and lime zest to make the dressing.
3. Pour the dressing over the mixed fruits and toss gently to coat.
4. Garnish with fresh mint leaves if desired.
5. Serve immediately or chill in the refrigerator until ready to enjoy.

**Nutrition Facts (per serving):**

- Calories: 80
- Protein: 1g
- Fat: 0g

- Carbohydrates: 21g
- Fiber: 3g

## Dark Chocolate Avocado Mousse

Prep Time: 10 mins

Total Time: 10 mins

Servings: 4 servings

**Ingredients:**

- 2 ripe avocados
- 1/4 cup unsweetened cocoa powder
- 1/4 cup honey or maple syrup
- 1 teaspoon vanilla extract
- Pinch of salt
- Fresh berries for garnish (optional)

**Directions:**

1. Cut the avocados in half, remove the pits, and scoop out the flesh into a food processor or blender.
2. Add cocoa powder, honey or maple syrup, vanilla extract, and a pinch of salt to the avocados.
3. Blend until smooth and creamy, scraping down the sides of the bowl as needed.
4. Divide the chocolate avocado mousse into serving dishes.
5. Chill in the refrigerator for at least 30 minutes before serving.
6. Garnish with fresh berries if desired.

**Nutrition Facts (per serving):**

- Calories: 200
- Protein: 3g

- Fat: 14g
- Carbohydrates: 20g
- Fiber: 7g

# Baked Apples with Cinnamon

Prep Time: 10 mins

Total Time: 40 mins

Servings: 4 servings

**Ingredients:**

- 4 large apples
- 2 tablespoons honey or maple syrup
- 1 teaspoon ground cinnamon
- 1/4 cup chopped nuts (e.g., walnuts, pecans, almonds)

**Directions:**

1. Preheat the oven to 375°F (190°C). Grease a baking dish with non-stick cooking spray.
2. Wash the apples and core them using an apple corer or a knife, leaving the bottoms intact.
3. In a small bowl, mix together honey or maple syrup and ground cinnamon.
4. Place the cored apples in the prepared baking dish.
5. Fill each apple cavity with the honey-cinnamon mixture.
6. Sprinkle chopped nuts over the top of each apple.
7. Bake in the preheated oven for 30-40 minutes, or until the apples are tender.
8. Remove from the oven and let cool slightly before serving.

9. Enjoy these baked apples warm, either on their own or topped with a dollop of Greek yogurt.

**Nutrition Facts (per serving):**

- Calories: 150
- Protein: 2g
- Fat: 4g
- Carbohydrates: 30g
- Fiber: 5g

# Chia Seed Pudding

Prep Time: 5 mins (plus chilling time)

Total Time: 4 hrs. 5 mins

Servings: 4 servings

**Ingredients:**

- 1/2 cup chia seeds
- 2 cups unsweetened almond milk or coconut milk
- 2 tablespoons honey or maple syrup
- 1 teaspoon vanilla extract
- Fresh berries for topping (optional)

**Directions:**

1. In a mixing bowl, whisk together chia seeds, almond milk or coconut milk, honey or maple syrup, and vanilla extract.
2. Cover the bowl and refrigerate for at least 4 hours or overnight, allowing the chia seeds to thicken and absorb the liquid.
3. Stir the chia seed pudding well before serving.
4. Divide the pudding into serving dishes and top with fresh berries if desired.

5.  Serve chilled and enjoy this creamy and nutritious dessert!

**Nutrition Facts (per serving):**

- Calories: 130
- Protein: 3g
- Fat: 7g
- Carbohydrates: 14g
- Fiber: 9g

# Baked Banana Oatmeal Cups

Prep Time: 10 mins

Total Time: 25 mins

Servings: 12 servings

**Ingredients:**

- 2 ripe bananas, mashed
- 2 cups rolled oats
- 1/4 cup honey or maple syrup
- 1/4 cup unsweetened applesauce
- 1 teaspoon vanilla extract
- 1/2 teaspoon ground cinnamon
- 1/4 teaspoon salt
- Optional add-ins: chopped nuts, dried fruits, chocolate chips

**Directions:**

1.  Preheat the oven to 350°F (175°C). Grease a muffin tin with non-stick cooking spray.
2.  In a mixing bowl, combine mashed bananas, rolled oats, honey or maple syrup, applesauce, vanilla extract, ground cinnamon, salt, and any optional add-ins of your choice.

3. Divide the oatmeal mixture evenly among the prepared muffin cups.

4. Bake in the preheated oven for 15-20 minutes, or until the tops are golden brown and set.

5. Remove from the oven and let cool in the muffin tin for a few minutes before transferring to a wire rack to cool completely.

6. Once cooled, store leftover oatmeal cups in an airtight container in the refrigerator.

7. Enjoy these baked banana oatmeal cups as a wholesome and delicious dessert or snack option!

**Nutrition Facts (per serving - 1 oatmeal cup):**

- Calories: 120
- Protein: 3g
- Fat: 2g
- Carbohydrates: 24g
- Fiber: 3g

# Blueberry Oatmeal Cookies

Prep Time: 10 mins

Total Time: 25 mins

Servings: 12 cookies

**Ingredients:**

- 1 cup rolled oats
- 1/2 cup almond flour
- 1/2 teaspoon baking powder
- 1/4 teaspoon salt
- 1/4 cup honey or maple syrup

- 1/4 cup unsweetened applesauce
- 1 tablespoon coconut oil, melted
- 1 teaspoon vanilla extract
- 1/2 cup fresh or frozen blueberries

**Directions:**

1. Preheat the oven to 350°F (175°C). Line a baking sheet with parchment paper.
2. In a mixing bowl, combine rolled oats, almond flour, baking powder, and salt.
3. In a separate bowl, whisk together honey or maple syrup, applesauce, melted coconut oil, and vanilla extract.
4. Add the wet ingredients to the dry ingredients and stir until well combined.
5. Gently fold in the blueberries.
6. Drop spoonfuls of the cookie dough onto the prepared baking sheet, spacing them apart.
7. Flatten each cookie slightly with the back of a spoon.
8. Bake in the preheated oven for 12-15 minutes, or until the edges are golden brown.
9. Remove from the oven and let the cookies cool on the baking sheet for 5 minutes before transferring them to a wire rack to cool completely.
10. Enjoy these delicious and wholesome blueberry oatmeal cookies as a guilt-free dessert or snack option!

**Nutrition Facts (per serving - 1 cookie):**

- Calories: 90

- Protein: 2g
- Fat: 3.5g
- Carbohydrates: 14g
- Fiber: 2g

# Chia Seed Chocolate Pudding

Prep Time: 5 mins (plus chilling time)

Total Time: 4 hrs. 5 mins

Servings: 4 servings

**Ingredients:**

- 1/4 cup chia seeds
- 1 cup unsweetened almond milk or coconut milk
- 2 tablespoons unsweetened cocoa powder
- 2 tablespoons honey or maple syrup
- 1/2 teaspoon vanilla extract
- Pinch of salt

**Directions:**

1. In a mixing bowl, whisk together chia seeds, almond milk or coconut milk, cocoa powder, honey or maple syrup, vanilla extract, and a pinch of salt.
2. Cover the bowl and refrigerate for at least 4 hours or overnight, allowing the chia seeds to thicken and absorb the liquid.
3. Stir the chocolate chia seed pudding well before serving.
4. Divide the pudding into serving dishes.
5. Serve chilled and enjoy this rich and creamy chocolate dessert!

**Nutrition Facts (per serving):**

- Calories: 100

- Protein: 3g
- Fat: 5g
- Carbohydrates: 14g
- Fiber: 6g

# Baked Peach Crisp

Prep Time: 15 mins

Total Time: 45 mins

Servings: 4 servings

**Ingredients:**

- 4 ripe peaches, sliced
- 1 tablespoon honey or maple syrup
- 1 teaspoon lemon juice
- 1/2 teaspoon ground cinnamon
- 1/4 teaspoon ground nutmeg
- 1/2 cup rolled oats
- 1/4 cup almond flour
- 2 tablespoons coconut oil, melted
- 2 tablespoons chopped almonds or pecans

**Directions:**

1. Preheat the oven to 350°F (175°C). Grease a baking dish with coconut oil or non-stick cooking spray.
2. In a mixing bowl, combine sliced peaches, honey or maple syrup, lemon juice, ground cinnamon, and ground nutmeg. Toss until the peaches are evenly coated.
3. Transfer the peach mixture to the prepared baking dish, spreading it out into an even layer.

4. In a separate bowl, mix together rolled oats, almond flour, melted coconut oil, and chopped almonds or pecans until crumbly.

5. Sprinkle the oat mixture over the top of the peaches in the baking dish.

6. Bake in the preheated oven for 25-30 minutes, or until the topping is golden brown and the peaches are bubbling.

7. Remove from the oven and let cool slightly before serving.

8. Enjoy this warm and comforting baked peach crisp as a delightful dessert!

**Nutrition Facts (per serving):**

- Calories: 180
- Protein: 4g
- Fat: 8g
- Carbohydrates: 26g
- Fiber: 5g

## Coconut Yogurt Parfait

Prep Time: 10 mins

Total Time: 10 mins

Servings: 2 servings

**Ingredients:**

- 1 cup unsweetened coconut yogurt
- 1/2 cup mixed berries (e.g., strawberries, blueberries, raspberries)
- 2 tablespoons unsweetened shredded coconut
- 2 tablespoons chopped nuts (e.g., almonds, walnuts)

**Directions:**

1.  In two serving glasses or bowls, layer coconut yogurt, mixed berries, shredded coconut, and chopped nuts.
2.  Repeat the layers until the glasses are filled.
3.  Serve immediately and enjoy this refreshing and nutritious coconut yogurt parfait!

**Nutrition Facts (per serving):**

*   Calories: 150
*   Protein: 4g
*   Fat: 9g
*   Carbohydrates: 12g
*   Fiber: 5g

# Frozen Banana Bites

Prep Time: 10 mins

Total Time: 2 hrs. 10 mins

Servings: 4 servings

**Ingredients:**

*   2 ripe bananas, peeled and cut into chunks
*   1/4 cup creamy almond butter or peanut butter
*   1/4 cup dark chocolate chips
*   1 tablespoon coconut oil

**Directions:**

1.  Line a baking sheet with parchment paper.
2.  Arrange banana chunks in a single layer on the prepared baking sheet.

3. In a small saucepan, melt almond butter or peanut butter with coconut oil and dark chocolate chips over low heat, stirring until smooth.

4. Drizzle the melted chocolate mixture over the banana chunks, covering them evenly.

5. Place the baking sheet in the freezer and freeze for at least 2 hours, or until the banana bites are firm.

6. Once frozen, remove from the freezer and transfer the banana bites to an airtight container for storage.

7. Enjoy these frozen banana bites straight from the freezer as a delicious and satisfying dessert or snack option!

**Nutrition Facts (per serving):**

- Calories: 160
- Protein: 3g
- Fat: 10g
- Carbohydrates: 18g
- Fiber: 3g

# Berry Chia Seed Pudding

Prep Time: 5 mins (plus chilling time)

Total Time: 4 hrs. 5 mins

Servings: 2 servings

**Ingredients:**

- 1/4 cup chia seeds
- 1 cup unsweetened almond milk or coconut milk
- 1 cup mixed berries (e.g., strawberries, blueberries, raspberries)
- 1 tablespoon honey or maple syrup

- 1/2 teaspoon vanilla extract
- Pinch of salt

**Directions:**

1. In a mixing bowl, whisk together chia seeds, almond milk or coconut milk, honey or maple syrup, vanilla extract, and a pinch of salt.
2. Cover the bowl and refrigerate for at least 4 hours or overnight, allowing the chia seeds to thicken and absorb the liquid.
3. In a blender, puree half of the mixed berries until smooth.
4. Once the chia seed pudding has set, divide it into serving glasses or bowls.
5. Pour the berry puree over the top of the pudding in each serving glass.
6. Garnish with the remaining mixed berries.
7. Serve chilled and enjoy this nutritious and flavorful berry chia seed pudding!

**Nutrition Facts (per serving):**

- Calories: 150
- Protein: 4g
- Fat: 6g
- Carbohydrates: 22g
- Fiber: 9g

# Cinnamon Baked Apples

Prep Time: 10 mins

Total Time: 40 mins

Servings: 2 servings

**Ingredients:**

- 2 apples (e.g., Granny Smith, Honey crisp), cored
- 2 tablespoons chopped nuts (e.g., walnuts, almonds, pecans)
- 1 tablespoon honey or maple syrup
- 1 teaspoon ground cinnamon
- 1/4 teaspoon nutmeg (optional)
- 1 tablespoon coconut oil, melted
- 1/4 cup water

**Directions:**

1. Preheat the oven to 375°F (190°C). Grease a baking dish with coconut oil.
2. In a small bowl, mix together chopped nuts, honey or maple syrup, ground cinnamon, and nutmeg (if using).
3. Stuff each cored apple with the nut mixture.
4. Place the stuffed apples in the prepared baking dish.
5. Drizzle melted coconut oil over the top of the stuffed apples.
6. Pour water into the bottom of the baking dish.
7. Bake in the preheated oven for 30-35 minutes, or until the apples are tender.
8. Remove from the oven and let cool slightly before serving.
9. Enjoy these warm and comforting cinnamon baked apples as a delightful dessert!

**Nutrition Facts (per serving):**

- Calories: 200
- Protein: 2g
- Fat: 9g

- Carbohydrates: 31g
- Fiber: 5g

# Coconut Almond Date Balls

Prep Time: 15 mins

Total Time: 15 mins

Servings: 8 balls

**Ingredients:**

- 1 cup pitted dates
- 1/2 cup shredded unsweetened coconut
- 1/2 cup almonds
- 1 tablespoon coconut oil, melted
- Pinch of salt

**Directions:**

1. In a food processor, combine pitted dates, shredded coconut, almonds, melted coconut oil, and a pinch of salt.
2. Process until the mixture forms a sticky dough.
3. Scoop out tablespoon-sized portions of the dough and roll them into balls.
4. Place the coconut almond date balls on a plate or baking sheet lined with parchment paper.
5. Refrigerate for at least 30 minutes to firm up.
6. Serve chilled and enjoy these delicious and energizing coconut almond date balls!

**Nutrition Facts (per serving - 1 ball):**

- Calories: 120
- Protein: 2g

- Fat: 6g
- Carbohydrates: 16g
- Fiber: 3g

## Greek Yogurt with Honey and Pistachios

Prep Time: 5 mins

Total Time: 5 mins

Servings: 2 servings

**Ingredients:**

- 1 cup plain Greek yogurt
- 2 tablespoons honey
- 2 tablespoons chopped pistachios

**Directions:**

1. Divide Greek yogurt into serving bowls.
2. Drizzle honey over the top of each serving of Greek yogurt.
3. Sprinkle chopped pistachios over the yogurt and honey.
4. Serve immediately and enjoy this creamy and indulgent Greek yogurt dessert!

**Nutrition Facts (per serving):**

- Calories: 180
- Protein: 12g
- Fat: 6g
- Carbohydrates: 20g
- Fiber: 1g

## Baked Pears with Cinnamon and Walnuts

Prep Time: 10 mins

Total Time: 30 mins

Servings: 2 servings

**Ingredients:**

- 2 ripe pears, halved and cored
- 2 tablespoons honey or maple syrup
- 1 teaspoon ground cinnamon
- 1/4 cup chopped walnuts

**Directions:**

1. Preheat the oven to 375°F (190°C). Grease a baking dish with coconut oil or non-stick cooking spray.
2. Place the pear halves, cut side up, in the prepared baking dish.
3. In a small bowl, mix together honey or maple syrup and ground cinnamon.
4. Drizzle the honey-cinnamon mixture over the top of each pear half.
5. Sprinkle chopped walnuts over the pears.
6. Bake in the preheated oven for 20-25 minutes, or until the pears are tender and caramelized.
7. Remove from the oven and let cool slightly before serving.
8. Enjoy these warm and fragrant baked pears as a delightful dessert!

**Nutrition Facts (per serving):**

- Calories: 200
- Protein: 2g
- Fat: 6g

- Carbohydrates: 40g
- Fiber: 6g

## Almond Butter Banana Bites

Prep Time: 10 mins

Total Time: 10 mins

Servings: 2 servings

**Ingredients:**

- 1 ripe banana
- 2 tablespoons almond butter
- 2 tablespoons unsweetened shredded coconut
- 2 tablespoons chopped almonds or walnuts

**Directions:**

1. Peel the banana and slice it into rounds, about 1/2 inch thick.
2. Spread almond butter onto half of the banana slices.
3. Top each almond butter-covered banana slice with another banana slice to make a sandwich.
4. Roll the edges of the banana sandwiches in shredded coconut until coated.
5. Insert a toothpick into each banana bite to hold it together.
6. Sprinkle chopped almonds or walnuts over the top of the banana bites.
7. Serve immediately or refrigerate for a firmer texture.
8. Enjoy these delightful almond butter banana bites as a nutritious and satisfying dessert or snack!

**Nutrition Facts (per serving):**

- Calories: 180

- Protein: 4g
- Fat: 12g
- Carbohydrates: 17g
- Fiber: 4g

## Greek Yogurt Parfait with Berries

Prep Time: 10 mins

Total Time: 10 mins

Servings: 2 servings

**Ingredients:**

- 1 cup plain Greek yogurt
- 1 cup mixed berries (e.g., strawberries, blueberries, raspberries)
- 2 tablespoons chopped nuts (e.g., almonds, walnuts, pecans)
- 2 tablespoons honey or maple syrup

**Directions:**

1. In serving glasses or bowls, layer plain Greek yogurt, mixed berries, and chopped nuts.
2. Drizzle honey or maple syrup over the top of each parfait.
3. Repeat the layers if desired.
4. Serve immediately and enjoy this simple yet delicious Greek yogurt parfait with berries!

**Nutrition Facts (per serving):**

- Calories: 220
- Protein: 16g
- Fat: 6g
- Carbohydrates: 28g
- Fiber: 4g

# Chocolate Avocado Pudding

Prep Time: 10 mins

Total Time: 10 mins

Servings: 2 servings

**Ingredients:**

- 1 ripe avocado
- 2 tablespoons unsweetened cocoa powder
- 2 tablespoons honey or maple syrup
- 1/2 teaspoon vanilla extract
- Pinch of salt
- 1/4 cup unsweetened almond milk or coconut milk

**Directions:**

1. In a blender or food processor, combine ripe avocado, unsweetened cocoa powder, honey or maple syrup, vanilla extract, salt, and almond milk or coconut milk.
2. Blend until smooth and creamy, scraping down the sides of the blender or food processor as needed.
3. Divide the chocolate avocado pudding into serving glasses or bowls.
4. Refrigerate for at least 30 minutes to chill and set.
5. Serve chilled and enjoy this rich and indulgent chocolate avocado pudding!

**Nutrition Facts (per serving):**

- Calories: 200
- Protein: 3g
- Fat: 12g

- Carbohydrates: 24g
- Fiber: 7g

# Fruit Salad with Mint Honey Dressing

Prep Time: 15 mins

Total Time: 15 mins

Servings: 2 servings

**Ingredients:**

- 1 cup mixed fresh fruit (e.g., strawberries, kiwi, pineapple, grapes)
- 1 tablespoon chopped fresh mint leaves
- 1 tablespoon honey
- 1 teaspoon lemon juice

**Directions:**

1. Wash and prepare the mixed fresh fruit as needed, cutting them into bite-sized pieces.
2. In a small bowl, whisk together chopped fresh mint leaves, honey, and lemon juice to make the dressing.
3. Pour the mint honey dressing over the mixed fresh fruit and gently toss to coat.
4. Divide the fruit salad into serving bowls or plates.
5. Serve immediately and enjoy this refreshing and naturally sweet fruit salad with mint honey dressing!

**Nutrition Facts (per serving):**

- Calories: 120
- Protein: 1g
- Fat: 0g

- Carbohydrates: 31g
- Fiber: 3g

## Baked Cinnamon Apple Slices

Prep Time: 10 mins

Total Time: 30 mins

Servings: 2 servings

**Ingredients:**

- 2 apples (e.g., Granny Smith, Honey crisp), cored and sliced
- 1 tablespoon honey or maple syrup
- 1 teaspoon ground cinnamon
- 1 tablespoon melted coconut oil

**Directions:**

1. Preheat the oven to 375°F (190°C). Grease a baking dish with coconut oil.
2. In a bowl, toss the apple slices with honey or maple syrup, ground cinnamon, and melted coconut oil until evenly coated.
3. Arrange the coated apple slices in a single layer in the prepared baking dish.
4. Bake in the preheated oven for 20-25 minutes, or until the apples are tender and lightly caramelized.
5. Remove from the oven and let cool slightly before serving.
6. Enjoy these warm and aromatic baked cinnamon apple slices as a delightful dessert or snack!

**Nutrition Facts (per serving):**

- Calories: 140
- Protein: 1g

- Fat: 4g
- Carbohydrates: 29g
- Fiber: 5g

# SEAFOOD RECIPES

## Grilled Lemon Herb Salmon

Prep Time: 10 mins

Total Time: 20 mins

Servings: 2

**Ingredients:**

- 2 salmon fillets (6 oz each), skin-on
- 2 tablespoons olive oil
- 1 tablespoon lemon juice
- 2 cloves garlic, minced
- 1 teaspoon fresh thyme leaves
- 1 teaspoon fresh rosemary leaves
- Salt and pepper, to taste
- Lemon slices (for garnish)

**Directions:**

1. Preheat the grill to medium-high heat.
2. In a small bowl, whisk together olive oil, lemon juice, minced garlic, thyme, and rosemary.
3. Place the salmon fillets on a plate and brush both sides with the lemon herb marinade. Season with salt and pepper.
4. Place the salmon fillets, skin-side down, on the preheated grill. Close the lid and grill for 4-5 minutes per side, or until the salmon is cooked through and flakes easily with a fork.
5. Remove the grilled salmon from the grill and transfer to a serving platter.

6. Garnish with lemon slices and additional fresh herbs if desired.

7. Serve immediately and enjoy this flavorful grilled lemon herb salmon!

**Nutrition Facts (per serving):**

- Calories: 350
- Protein: 34g
- Fat: 22g
- Carbohydrates: 1g
- Fiber: 0g

# Baked Lemon Garlic Shrimp

Prep Time: 10 mins

Total Time: 20 mins

Servings: 2

**Ingredients:**

- 1/2 lb. large shrimp, peeled and deveined
- 2 tablespoons olive oil
- 2 cloves garlic, minced
- 1 tablespoon lemon juice
- 1 teaspoon lemon zest
- 1 tablespoon chopped fresh parsley
- Salt and pepper, to taste

**Directions:**

1. Preheat the oven to 400°F (200°C). Grease a baking dish with olive oil.

2. In a bowl, toss the shrimp with olive oil, minced garlic, lemon juice, lemon zest, chopped parsley, salt, and pepper until evenly coated.

3. Arrange the seasoned shrimp in a single layer in the prepared baking dish.

4. Bake in the preheated oven for 8-10 minutes, or until the shrimp are pink and cooked through.

5. Remove from the oven and let cool slightly before serving.

6. Serve these delicious baked lemon garlic shrimp as a flavorful and healthy seafood dish!

**Nutrition Facts (per serving):**

- Calories: 180
- Protein: 20g
- Fat: 10g
- Carbohydrates: 3g
- Fiber: 0g

# Pan-Seared Scallops with Lemon Butter Sauce

Prep Time: 10 mins

Total Time: 10 mins

Servings: 2

**Ingredients:**

- 6 large scallops
- Salt and pepper, to taste
- 2 tablespoons olive oil
- 2 tablespoons unsalted butter
- 2 cloves garlic, minced

- 1 tablespoon lemon juice
- 1 tablespoon chopped fresh parsley

**Directions:**

1. Pat the scallops dry with paper towels and season both sides with salt and pepper.
2. Heat olive oil in a large skillet over medium-high heat.
3. Add the scallops to the skillet and cook for 2-3 minutes on each side, or until golden brown and cooked through.
4. Remove the cooked scallops from the skillet and transfer to a plate. Cover with foil to keep warm.
5. In the same skillet, melt the butter over medium heat. Add minced garlic and cook for 1 minute, or until fragrant.
6. Remove the skillet from the heat and stir in lemon juice and chopped parsley.
7. Pour the lemon butter sauce over the cooked scallops.
8. Serve immediately and enjoy these succulent pan-seared scallops with lemon butter sauce!

**Nutrition Facts (per serving):**

- Calories: 220
- Protein: 18g
- Fat: 15g
- Carbohydrates: 2g
- Fiber: 0g

# Grilled Garlic Herb Shrimp Skewers

Prep Time: 20 mins (includes marinating time)

Total Time: 30 mins

Servings: 2

**Ingredients:**

- 1/2 lb. large shrimp, peeled and deveined
- 2 tablespoons olive oil
- 2 cloves garlic, minced
- 1 tablespoon chopped fresh parsley
- 1 teaspoon chopped fresh thyme
- 1 teaspoon chopped fresh rosemary
- Salt and pepper, to taste
- Lemon wedges (for serving)

**Directions:**

1. In a bowl, combine olive oil, minced garlic, chopped parsley, thyme, rosemary, salt, and pepper.
2. Add the peeled and deveined shrimp to the marinade and toss to coat. Cover and refrigerate for at least 15 minutes.
3. Preheat the grill to medium-high heat. Thread the marinated shrimp onto skewers.
4. Grill the shrimp skewers for 2-3 minutes on each side, or until the shrimp are pink and opaque.
5. Remove from the grill and transfer the grilled shrimp skewers to a serving platter.
6. Serve with lemon wedges for squeezing over the shrimp.
7. Enjoy these flavorful grilled garlic herb shrimp skewers as a tasty and nutritious seafood dish!

**Nutrition Facts (per serving):**

- Calories: 190
- Protein: 20g
- Fat: 12g
- Carbohydrates: 2g
- Fiber: 0g

## Baked Lemon Dijon Salmon

Prep Time: 10 mins

Total Time: 20 mins

Servings: 2

**Ingredients:**

- 2 salmon fillets (6 oz each)
- 2 tablespoons Dijon mustard
- 2 tablespoons olive oil
- 1 tablespoon lemon juice
- 2 cloves garlic, minced
- 1 teaspoon lemon zest
- Salt and pepper, to taste

**Directions:**

1. Preheat the oven to 400°F (200°C). Grease a baking dish with olive oil.
2. In a small bowl, whisk together Dijon mustard, olive oil, lemon juice, minced garlic, lemon zest, salt, and pepper.
3. Place the salmon fillets in the prepared baking dish and brush the Dijon mustard mixture over the top of each fillet.

4. Bake in the preheated oven for 12-15 minutes, or until the salmon is cooked through and flakes easily with a fork.

5. Remove from the oven and let cool slightly before serving.

6. Serve this flavorful baked lemon Dijon salmon with your favorite side dishes.

7. Enjoy this delicious and nutritious seafood dish!

**Nutrition Facts (per serving):**

- Calories: 320
- Protein: 34g
- Fat: 18g
- Carbohydrates: 2g
- Fiber: 0g

# Lemon Garlic Shrimp Pasta

Prep Time: 10 mins

Total Time: 20 mins

Servings: 2

**Ingredients:**

- 8 oz whole wheat spaghetti
- 1/2 lb. large shrimp, peeled and deveined
- 2 tablespoons olive oil
- 3 cloves garlic, minced
- 1 tablespoon lemon juice
- 1 teaspoon lemon zest
- Salt and pepper, to taste
- 2 tablespoons chopped fresh parsley
- Grated Parmesan cheese (optional, for serving)

**Directions:**

1. Cook the spaghetti according to package instructions until al dente. Drain and set aside.

2. In a large skillet, heat olive oil over medium heat. Add minced garlic and cook for 1 minute, or until fragrant.

3. Add the shrimp to the skillet and cook for 2-3 minutes on each side, or until pink and cooked through.

4. Stir in lemon juice, lemon zest, salt, pepper, and chopped parsley.

5. Add the cooked spaghetti to the skillet and toss to coat with the shrimp and lemon garlic sauce.

6. Cook for an additional 1-2 minutes, stirring occasionally, until heated through.

7. Serve the lemon garlic shrimp pasta hot, garnished with grated Parmesan cheese if desired.

**Nutritional Information (per serving):**

- Calories: 430
- Protein: 26g
- Fat: 14g
- Carbohydrates: 53g
- Fiber: 6g

# Grilled Salmon with Avocado Salsa

Prep Time: 10 mins

Total Time: 20 mins

Servings: 2

**Ingredients:**

- 2 salmon fillets (6 oz each)
- 1 tablespoon olive oil
- Salt and pepper, to taste
- 1 avocado, diced
- 1 tomato, diced
- 1/4 red onion, finely chopped
- 1 tablespoon chopped fresh cilantro
- 1 tablespoon lime juice

**Directions:**

1. Preheat the grill to medium-high heat. Brush the salmon fillets with olive oil and season with salt and pepper.
2. Grill the salmon fillets for 4-5 minutes on each side, or until cooked through and flaky.
3. In a bowl, combine diced avocado, tomato, red onion, cilantro, and lime juice to make the avocado salsa.
4. Serve the grilled salmon topped with avocado salsa.

**Nutritional Information (per serving):**

- Calories: 380
- Protein: 26g
- Fat: 25g
- Carbohydrates: 12g
- Fiber: 6g

# Shrimp and Vegetable Stir-Fry

Prep Time: 15 mins

Total Time: 20 mins

Servings: 2

**Ingredients:**

- 1/2 lb. large shrimp, peeled and deveined
- 2 tablespoons olive oil
- 2 cloves garlic, minced
- 1 bell pepper, thinly sliced
- 1 cup broccoli florets
- 1 carrot, thinly sliced
- 1/4 cup low-sodium soy sauce
- 1 tablespoon honey
- 1 teaspoon sesame oil
- 1 tablespoon cornstarch
- Cooked brown rice, for serving

**Directions:**

1. In a small bowl, whisk together soy sauce, honey, sesame oil, and cornstarch to make the sauce. Set aside.

2. Heat olive oil in a large skillet or wok over medium-high heat. Add minced garlic and cook for 1 minute.

3. Add shrimp to the skillet and cook for 2-3 minutes on each side, or until pink and cooked through. Remove shrimp from the skillet and set aside.

4. In the same skillet, add bell pepper, broccoli, and carrot. Stir-fry for 3-4 minutes, or until vegetables are tender-crisp.

5. Return the cooked shrimp to the skillet and pour the sauce over the shrimp and vegetables. Cook for an additional 1-2 minutes, stirring constantly, until the sauce thickens.

6. Serve the shrimp and vegetable stir-fry hot over cooked brown rice.

**Nutritional Information (per serving):**

- Calories: 350
- Protein: 25g
- Fat: 14g
- Carbohydrates: 30g
- Fiber: 5g

## Tuna Salad Stuffed Avocados

Prep Time: 10 mins

Total Time: 10 mins

Servings: 2

**Ingredients:**

- 1 can (5 oz) tuna, drained
- 2 ripe avocados
- 1/4 cup diced cucumber
- 1/4 cup diced red bell pepper
- 2 tablespoons chopped fresh parsley
- 1 tablespoon lemon juice
- Salt and pepper, to taste

**Directions:**

1. Cut the avocados in half and remove the pits. Scoop out some of the flesh from each avocado half to create a larger cavity for the filling.

2. In a bowl, combine drained tuna, diced cucumber, diced red bell pepper, chopped parsley, lemon juice, salt, and pepper. Mix until well combined.

3. Spoon the tuna salad mixture into the avocado halves, dividing evenly.

4. Serve the tuna salad stuffed avocados immediately as a delicious and nutritious seafood snack or light meal.

**Nutritional Information (per serving):**

- Calories: 280
- Protein: 18g
- Fat: 20g
- Carbohydrates: 12g
- Fiber: 9g

# Baked Cod with Lemon Herb Crust

Prep Time: 10 mins

Total Time: 20 mins

Servings: 2

**Ingredients:**

- 2 cod fillets (6 oz each)
- 1 tablespoon olive oil
- 1 tablespoon lemon juice
- 1 teaspoon lemon zest
- 1 tablespoon chopped fresh parsley
- 1 tablespoon chopped fresh dill
- Salt and pepper, to taste
- Lemon wedges (for serving)

**Directions:**

1. Preheat the oven to 400°F (200°C). Grease a baking dish with olive oil.

2. In a small bowl, combine olive oil, lemon juice, lemon zest, chopped parsley, chopped dill, salt, and pepper.

3. Place the cod fillets in the prepared baking dish and brush both sides with the lemon herb mixture.

4. Bake in the preheated oven for 12-15 minutes, or until the cod is opaque and flakes easily with a fork.

5. Remove from the oven and serve the baked cod hot, garnished with lemon wedges.

**Nutritional Information (per serving):**

- Calories: 260
- Protein: 26g
- Fat: 10g
- Carbohydrates: 2g
- Fiber: 1g

## Herb-Crusted Baked Salmon

Prep Time: 10 mins

Total Time: 25 mins

Servings: 2

**Ingredients:**

- 2 salmon fillets (6 oz each)
- 2 tablespoons whole wheat breadcrumbs
- 1 tablespoon chopped fresh parsley
- 1 tablespoon chopped fresh dill

- 1 tablespoon olive oil
- 1 tablespoon Dijon mustard
- Salt and pepper, to taste
- Lemon wedges (for serving)

**Directions:**

1. Preheat the oven to 400°F (200°C). Line a baking sheet with parchment paper.

2. In a small bowl, combine breadcrumbs, chopped parsley, chopped dill, olive oil, Dijon mustard, salt, and pepper to form the herb crust.

3. Place the salmon fillets on the prepared baking sheet. Spread the herb crust mixture evenly over the top of each fillet, pressing gently to adhere.

4. Bake in the preheated oven for 12-15 minutes, or until the salmon is cooked through and flakes easily with a fork.

5. Remove from the oven and serve the herb-crusted baked salmon hot, garnished with lemon wedges.

**Nutritional Information (per serving):**

- Calories: 320
- Protein: 26g
- Fat: 20g
- Carbohydrates: 4g
- Fiber: 1g

## Coconut Shrimp with Mango Salsa

Prep Time: 15 mins

Total Time: 20 mins

Servings: 2

**Ingredients:**

- 1/2 lb. large shrimp, peeled and deveined
- 1/2 cup unsweetened shredded coconut
- 1 egg, beaten
- 1/4 cup whole wheat flour
- 1/2 teaspoon paprika
- Salt and pepper, to taste
- 1 mango, diced
- 1/4 cup diced red bell pepper
- 1/4 cup chopped fresh cilantro
- 1 tablespoon lime juice

**Directions:**

1. Preheat the oven to 400°F (200°C). Line a baking sheet with parchment paper.

2. In separate bowls, place beaten egg, whole wheat flour mixed with paprika, and shredded coconut.

3. Dip each shrimp into the flour mixture, then into the beaten egg, and finally into the shredded coconut, pressing gently to coat.

4. Place the coated shrimp on the prepared baking sheet. Season with salt and pepper.

5. Bake in the preheated oven for 10-12 minutes, or until the coconut coating is golden brown and the shrimp are cooked through.

6. In the meantime, prepare the mango salsa by combining diced mango, diced red bell pepper, chopped cilantro, and lime juice in a bowl.
7. Serve the coconut shrimp hot with mango salsa on the side.

**Nutritional Information (per serving):**

- Calories: 290
- Protein: 20g
- Fat: 12g
- Carbohydrates: 25g
- Fiber: 5g

## Tilapia Picasa

Prep Time: 10 mins

Total Time: 20 mins

Servings: 2

**Ingredients:**

- 2 tilapia fillets (6 oz each)
- 2 tablespoons whole wheat flour
- 2 tablespoons olive oil
- 2 tablespoons lemon juice
- 1/4 cup low-sodium chicken broth
- 2 tablespoons capers, drained
- 2 tablespoons chopped fresh parsley
- Salt and pepper, to taste

**Directions:**

1. Season the tilapia fillets with salt and pepper, then dredge them in whole wheat flour, shaking off any excess.

2. Heat olive oil in a large skillet over medium-high heat. Add the tilapia fillets and cook for 3-4 minutes on each side, or until golden brown and cooked through. Remove from skillet and set aside.

3. In the same skillet, add lemon juice, chicken broth, and capers. Bring to a simmer and cook for 2 minutes, stirring occasionally.

4. Return the cooked tilapia fillets to the skillet, spooning the sauce over the top.

5. Cook for an additional 1-2 minutes, until the fish is heated through.

6. Serve the tilapia picante hot, garnished with chopped fresh parsley.

**Nutritional Information (per serving):**

- Calories: 280
- Protein: 30g
- Fat: 14g
- Carbohydrates: 8g
- Fiber: 1g

## Grilled Halibut with Lemon Herb Sauce

Prep Time: 15 mins

Total Time: 20 mins

Servings: 2

**Ingredients:**

- 2 halibut fillets (6 oz each)
- 1 tablespoon olive oil
- 1 tablespoon lemon juice

- 1 teaspoon lemon zest
- 1 tablespoon chopped fresh parsley
- 1 tablespoon chopped fresh dill
- Salt and pepper, to taste

**Directions:**

1. Preheat the grill to medium-high heat. Brush halibut fillets with olive oil and season with salt and pepper.
2. In a small bowl, combine lemon juice, lemon zest, chopped parsley, and chopped dill to make the lemon herb sauce.
3. Grill the halibut fillets for 3-4 minutes on each side, or until cooked through and opaque.
4. Remove the grilled halibut from the grill and drizzle with the lemon herb sauce.
5. Serve the grilled halibut hot, garnished with additional chopped fresh parsley and dill if desired.

**Nutritional Information (per serving):**

- Calories: 290
- Protein: 28g
- Fat: 12g
- Carbohydrates: 2g
- Fiber: 1g

## Lemon Garlic Shrimp with Quinoa

Prep Time: 10 mins

Total Time: 20 mins

Servings: 2

**Ingredients:**

- 1 cup quinoa, rinsed
- 1 lb. large shrimp, peeled and deveined
- 2 tablespoons olive oil
- 3 cloves garlic, minced
- Zest and juice of 1 lemon
- Salt and pepper, to taste
- Chopped fresh parsley, for garnish

**Directions:**

1. In a medium saucepan, bring 2 cups of water to a boil. Add the quinoa, reduce heat to low, cover, and simmer for 15 minutes, or until quinoa is tender and water is absorbed.
2. In a large skillet, heat olive oil over medium-high heat. Add minced garlic and cook for 1 minute, or until fragrant.
3. Add the shrimp to the skillet and cook for 2-3 minutes on each side, or until pink and cooked through.
4. Stir in lemon zest and lemon juice. Season with salt and pepper to taste.
5. Serve the lemon garlic shrimp over cooked quinoa, garnished with chopped fresh parsley.

**Nutritional Information (per serving):**

- Calories: 430
- Protein: 36g
- Fat: 14g
- Carbohydrates: 39g
- Fiber: 4g

# Baked Cod with Tomato Basil Relish

Prep Time: 15 mins

Total Time: 25 mins

Servings: 2

**Ingredients:**

- 2 cod fillets (6 oz each)
- 1 cup cherry tomatoes, halved
- 2 tablespoons chopped fresh basil
- 1 tablespoon olive oil
- 1 tablespoon balsamic vinegar
- Salt and pepper, to taste

**Directions:**

1. Preheat the oven to 400°F (200°C). Line a baking sheet with parchment paper.
2. Place the cod fillets on the prepared baking sheet. Season with salt and pepper.
3. In a small bowl, combine cherry tomatoes, chopped basil, olive oil, and balsamic vinegar to make the tomato basil relish.
4. Spoon the tomato basil relish over the top of each cod fillet.
5. Bake in the preheated oven for 12-15 minutes, or until the cod is cooked through and flakes easily with a fork.
6. Serve the baked cod hot, topped with additional tomato basil relish if desired.

**Nutritional Information (per serving):**

- Calories: 270
- Protein: 32g
- Fat: 10g

- Carbohydrates: 10g
- Fiber: 2g

## Cajun Grilled Shrimp Skewers

Prep Time: 15 mins

Total Time: 20 mins

Servings: 2

**Ingredients:**

- 1 lb. large shrimp, peeled and deveined
- 2 tablespoons olive oil
- 1 tablespoon Cajun seasoning
- 1 tablespoon lemon juice
- Salt and pepper, to taste
- Lemon wedges, for serving

**Directions:**

1. Preheat the grill to medium-high heat.
2. In a bowl, toss the shrimp with olive oil, Cajun seasoning, lemon juice, salt, and pepper until evenly coated.
3. Thread the seasoned shrimp onto skewers.
4. Grill the shrimp skewers for 2-3 minutes on each side, or until pink and cooked through.
5. Remove from the grill and serve the Cajun grilled shrimp skewers hot, with lemon wedges on the side.

**Nutritional Information (per serving):**

- Calories: 240
- Protein: 30g
- Fat: 12g

- Carbohydrates: 2g
- Fiber: 0g

## Salmon Cakes with Avocado Yogurt Sauce

Prep Time: 15 mins

Total Time: 25 mins

Servings: 2

**Ingredients:**

- 1 can (6 oz) wild-caught salmon, drained and flaked
- 1/4 cup whole wheat breadcrumbs
- 1 egg, beaten
- 2 tablespoons chopped fresh parsley
- 1 tablespoon chopped fresh dill
- 1/4 teaspoon garlic powder
- Salt and pepper, to taste
- 1 tablespoon olive oil
- 1 avocado, mashed
- 1/4 cup plain Greek yogurt
- 1 tablespoon lemon juice

**Directions:**

1. In a bowl, combine flaked salmon, breadcrumbs, beaten egg, chopped parsley, chopped dill, garlic powder, salt, and pepper. Mix until well combined.
2. Form the salmon mixture into patties.
3. Heat olive oil in a skillet over medium heat. Cook salmon cakes for 3-4 minutes on each side, or until golden brown and heated through.

4. In a small bowl, mix mashed avocado, Greek yogurt, and lemon juice to make the avocado yogurt sauce.

5. Serve the salmon cakes hot, topped with avocado yogurt sauce.

**Nutritional Information (per serving):**

- Calories: 320
- Protein: 25g
- Fat: 20g
- Carbohydrates: 15g
- Fiber: 6g

# SOUP RECIPES

## Creamy Butternut Squash Soup

Prep Time: 15 mins

Total Time: 45 mins

Servings: 4

**Ingredients:**

- 1 medium butternut squash, peeled, seeded, and diced
- 1 tablespoon olive oil
- 1 onion, chopped
- 2 cloves garlic, minced
- 4 cups vegetable broth
- 1 teaspoon dried thyme
- 1/2 teaspoon ground nutmeg
- Salt and pepper, to taste
- 1/2 cup coconut milk
- Fresh parsley, for garnish (optional)

**Directions:**

1. In a large pot, heat olive oil over medium heat. Add chopped onion and minced garlic, and cook until softened, about 5 minutes.

2. Add diced butternut squash to the pot along with vegetable broth, dried thyme, ground nutmeg, salt, and pepper. Bring to a boil, then reduce heat to low and simmer for 25-30 minutes, or until squash is tender.

3. Use an immersion blender to puree the soup until smooth. Alternatively, carefully transfer the soup to a blender and blend until smooth, then return to the pot.
4. Stir in coconut milk and cook for an additional 5 minutes, until heated through.
5. Serve the creamy butternut squash soup hot, garnished with fresh parsley if desired.

**Nutritional Information (per serving):**

- Calories: 170
- Protein: 3g
- Fat: 8g
- Carbohydrates: 25g
- Fiber: 6g

# Lentil and Vegetable Soup

Prep Time: 15 mins

Total Time: 45 mins

Servings: 4

**Ingredients:**

- 1 cup dried green lentils, rinsed
- 1 tablespoon olive oil
- 1 onion, chopped
- 2 carrots, diced
- 2 celery stalks, diced
- 2 cloves garlic, minced
- 6 cups vegetable broth
- 1 can (14 oz) diced tomatoes

184

- 1 teaspoon ground cumin
- 1 teaspoon paprika
- Salt and pepper, to taste
- Fresh parsley, for garnish (optional)

**Directions:**

1. In a large pot, heat olive oil over medium heat. Add chopped onion, diced carrots, diced celery, and minced garlic. Cook until vegetables are softened, about 5 minutes.

2. Add rinsed lentils, vegetable broth, diced tomatoes, ground cumin, paprika, salt, and pepper to the pot. Bring to a boil, then reduce heat to low and simmer for 25-30 minutes, or until lentils are tender.

3. Taste and adjust seasoning if necessary.

4. Serve the lentil and vegetable soup hot, garnished with fresh parsley if desired.

**Nutritional Information (per serving):**

- Calories: 250
- Protein: 15g
- Fat: 4g
- Carbohydrates: 40g
- Fiber: 15g

## Coconut Curry Shrimp Soup

Prep Time: 15 mins

Total Time: 30 mins

Servings: 4

**Ingredients:**

- 1 lb. shrimp, peeled and deveined
- 1 tablespoon olive oil
- 1 onion, chopped
- 2 cloves garlic, minced
- 1 tablespoon curry powder
- 1 can (14 oz) coconut milk
- 4 cups vegetable broth
- 1 bell pepper, diced
- 1 cup sliced mushrooms
- 2 cups baby spinach
- Salt and pepper, to taste
- Fresh cilantro, for garnish (optional)

**Directions:**

1. In a large pot, heat olive oil over medium heat. Add chopped onion and minced garlic, and cook until softened, about 5 minutes.
2. Stir in curry powder and cook for 1 minute, until fragrant.
3. Add coconut milk and vegetable broth to the pot, and bring to a simmer.
4. Add diced bell pepper and sliced mushrooms, and simmer for 5 minutes.
5. Add shrimp and baby spinach to the pot, and cook for an additional 3-4 minutes, or until shrimp is pink and cooked through.
6. Season with salt and pepper to taste.

7. Serve the coconut curry shrimp soup hot, garnished with fresh cilantro if desired.

**Nutritional Information (per serving):**

- Calories: 290
- Protein: 20g
- Fat: 20g
- Carbohydrates: 10g
- Fiber: 3g

# Tomato Basil Soup

Prep Time: 10 mins

Total Time: 35 mins

Servings: 4

**Ingredients:**

- 2 tablespoons olive oil
- 1 onion, chopped
- 2 cloves garlic, minced
- 1 can (28 oz) crushed tomatoes
- 4 cups vegetable broth
- 1/4 cup chopped fresh basil
- Salt and pepper, to taste
- 1/4 cup plain Greek yogurt, for serving (optional)

**Directions:**

1. In a large pot, heat olive oil over medium heat. Add chopped onion and minced garlic, and cook until softened, about 5 minutes.

2. Add crushed tomatoes and vegetable broth to the pot, and bring to a simmer.
3. Simmer the soup for 20 minutes, stirring occasionally.
4. Stir in chopped fresh basil, and season with salt and pepper to taste.
5. Use an immersion blender to puree the soup until smooth. Alternatively, carefully transfer the soup to a blender and blend until smooth, then return to the pot.
6. Serve the tomato basil soup hot, with a dollop of plain Greek yogurt on top if desired.

**Nutritional Information (per serving):**

- Calories: 140
- Protein: 4g
- Fat: 7g
- Carbohydrates: 17g
- Fiber: 4g

## Miso Soup with Tofu and Seaweed

Prep Time: 10 mins

Total Time: 20 mins

Servings: 4

**Ingredients:**

- 4 cups vegetable broth
- 2 tablespoons white miso paste
- 1 block (12 oz) firm tofu, diced
- 2 green onions, thinly sliced
- 1 sheet nori seaweed, torn into small pieces

- 1 tablespoon soy sauce
- 1 teaspoon sesame oil
- 1 teaspoon rice vinegar
- 1 teaspoon grated fresh ginger

**Directions:**

1. In a large pot, bring vegetable broth to a simmer over medium heat.
2. In a small bowl, whisk together white miso paste and a ladleful of hot broth until smooth. Stir the miso mixture back into the pot.
3. Add diced tofu, sliced green onions, torn nori seaweed, soy sauce, sesame oil, rice vinegar, and grated fresh ginger to the pot. Simmer for 5 minutes.
4. Taste and adjust seasoning if necessary.
5. Serve the miso soup hot.

**Nutritional Information (per serving):**

- Calories: 150
- Protein: 11g
- Fat: 8g
- Carbohydrates: 10g
- Fiber: 2g

# Creamy Spinach and Chickpea Soup

Prep Time: 10 mins

Total Time: 30 mins

Servings: 4

**Ingredients:**

- 1 tablespoon olive oil
- 1 onion, chopped
- 2 cloves garlic, minced
- 4 cups vegetable broth
- 2 cups chopped spinach
- 1 can (15 oz) chickpeas, drained and rinsed
- 1/2 teaspoon ground cumin
- 1/2 teaspoon ground coriander
- Salt and pepper, to taste
- 1/4 cup plain Greek yogurt, for serving (optional)
- Fresh cilantro, for garnish (optional)

**Directions:**

1. Heat olive oil in a large pot over medium heat. Add chopped onion and minced garlic, and cook until softened, about 5 minutes.
2. Pour vegetable broth into the pot and bring to a simmer.
3. Add chopped spinach, chickpeas, ground cumin, and ground coriander to the pot. Simmer for 15 minutes.
4. Use an immersion blender to blend the soup until smooth. Alternatively, carefully transfer the soup to a blender and blend until smooth, then return to the pot.
5. Season with salt and pepper to taste.
6. Serve the creamy spinach and chickpea soup hot, with a dollop of plain Greek yogurt on top and garnished with fresh cilantro if desired.

**Nutritional Information (per serving):**

- Calories: 180
- Protein: 9g
- Fat: 5g
- Carbohydrates: 26g
- Fiber: 6g

## Vegetable Quinoa Soup

Prep Time: 15 mins

Total Time: 40 mins

Servings: 4

**Ingredients:**

- 1 tablespoon olive oil
- 1 onion, chopped
- 2 cloves garlic, minced
- 4 cups vegetable broth
- 1 can (14 oz) diced tomatoes
- 1 cup cooked quinoa
- 2 carrots, diced
- 2 celery stalks, diced
- 1 zucchini, diced
- 1 teaspoon dried thyme
- Salt and pepper, to taste
- Fresh parsley, for garnish (optional)

**Directions:**

1. Heat olive oil in a large pot over medium heat. Add chopped onion and minced garlic, and cook until softened, about 5 minutes.

2. Pour vegetable broth into the pot and bring to a simmer.

3. Add diced tomatoes, cooked quinoa, diced carrots, diced celery, diced zucchini, dried thyme, salt, and pepper to the pot. Simmer for 20 minutes.

4. Taste and adjust seasoning if necessary.

5. Serve the vegetable quinoa soup hot, garnished with fresh parsley if desired.

**Nutritional Information (per serving):**

- Calories: 220
- Protein: 7g
- Fat: 5g
- Carbohydrates: 38g
- Fiber: 7g

# Ginger Carrot Soup

Prep Time: 10 mins

Total Time: 30 mins

Servings: 4

**Ingredients:**

- 1 tablespoon olive oil
- 1 onion, chopped
- 2 cloves garlic, minced
- 1 tablespoon fresh ginger, grated
- 6 cups vegetable broth
- 1 lb. carrots, peeled and chopped
- 1 potato, peeled and chopped
- Salt and pepper, to taste

- 2 tablespoons fresh lemon juice
- Fresh cilantro, for garnish (optional)

**Directions:**

1. Heat olive oil in a large pot over medium heat. Add chopped onion, minced garlic, and grated ginger, and cook until softened, about 5 minutes.

2. Pour vegetable broth into the pot and bring to a simmer.

3. Add chopped carrots and chopped potato to the pot. Simmer for 15-20 minutes, or until vegetables are tender.

4. Use an immersion blender to blend the soup until smooth. Alternatively, carefully transfer the soup to a blender and blend until smooth, then return to the pot.

5. Season with salt, pepper, and fresh lemon juice to taste.

6. Serve the ginger carrot soup hot, garnished with fresh cilantro if desired.

**Nutritional Information (per serving):**

- Calories: 140
- Protein: 3g
- Fat: 4g
- Carbohydrates: 24g
- Fiber: 5g

## Creamy Mushroom Soup

Prep Time: 10 mins

Total Time: 35 mins

Servings: 4

**Ingredients:**

- 1 tablespoon olive oil
- 1 onion, chopped
- 2 cloves garlic, minced
- 8 oz mushrooms, sliced
- 4 cups vegetable broth
- 1 tablespoon soy sauce
- 1 tablespoon nutritional yeast
- Salt and pepper, to taste
- 1/4 cup plain Greek yogurt, for serving (optional)
- Fresh parsley, for garnish (optional)

**Directions:**

1. Heat olive oil in a large pot over medium heat. Add chopped onion and minced garlic, and cook until softened, about 5 minutes.
2. Add sliced mushrooms to the pot and cook until they release their moisture and start to brown, about 8 minutes.
3. Pour vegetable broth into the pot and bring to a simmer.
4. Stir in soy sauce and nutritional yeast. Simmer for 10 minutes.
5. Use an immersion blender to blend the soup until smooth. Alternatively, carefully transfer the soup to a blender and blend until smooth, then return to the pot.
6. Season with salt and pepper to taste.
7. Serve the creamy mushroom soup hot, with a dollop of plain Greek yogurt on top and garnished with fresh parsley if desired.

**Nutritional Information (per serving):**

- Calories: 120

- Protein: 6g
- Fat: 4g
- Carbohydrates: 16g
- Fiber: 3g

# Lentil Vegetable Soup

Prep Time: 15 mins

Total Time: 40 mins

Servings: 4

**Ingredients:**

- 1 tablespoon olive oil
- 1 onion, chopped
- 2 cloves garlic, minced
- 1 carrot, diced
- 1 celery stalk, diced
- 1 cup dry green lentils, rinsed
- 4 cups vegetable broth
- 1 can (14 oz) diced tomatoes
- 1 teaspoon ground cumin
- 1 teaspoon ground coriander
- Salt and pepper, to taste
- Fresh parsley, for garnish (optional)

**Directions:**

1. Heat olive oil in a large pot over medium heat. Add chopped onion and minced garlic, and cook until softened, about 5 minutes.

2. Add diced carrot and diced celery to the pot, and cook for another 5 minutes.

3. Stir in dry green lentils, vegetable broth, diced tomatoes, ground cumin, and ground coriander. Bring to a simmer and cook for 25-30 minutes, or until lentils are tender.

4. Taste and adjust seasoning if necessary.

5. Serve the lentil vegetable soup hot, garnished with fresh parsley if desired.

**Nutritional Information (per serving):**

- Calories: 240
- Protein: 13g
- Fat: 3g
- Carbohydrates: 42g
- Fiber: 15g

## Detox Lentil Soup

Prep Time: 15 mins

Total Time: 45 mins

Servings: 4

**Ingredients:**

- 1 tablespoon olive oil
- 1 onion, chopped
- 2 cloves garlic, minced
- 2 carrots, diced
- 2 celery stalks, diced
- 1 cup dry green lentils, rinsed
- 4 cups vegetable broth

- 1 teaspoon ground cumin
- 1 teaspoon ground turmeric
- Salt and pepper, to taste
- Fresh parsley, for garnish (optional)
- Lemon wedges, for serving (optional)

**Directions:**

1. Heat olive oil in a large pot over medium heat. Add chopped onion and minced garlic, and cook until softened, about 5 minutes.
2. Add diced carrots and diced celery to the pot, and cook for another 5 minutes.
3. Stir in dry green lentils, vegetable broth, ground cumin, and ground turmeric. Bring to a simmer and cook for 25-30 minutes, or until lentils are tender.
4. Taste and adjust seasoning if necessary.
5. Serve the detox lentil soup hot, garnished with fresh parsley and lemon wedges if desired.

**Nutritional Information (per serving):**

- Calories: 220
- Protein: 12g
- Fat: 4g
- Carbohydrates: 36g
- Fiber: 15g

## Creamy Cauliflower Soup

Prep Time: 10 mins

Total Time: 30 mins

Servings: 4

**Ingredients:**

- 1 tablespoon olive oil
- 1 onion, chopped
- 2 cloves garlic, minced
- 1 head cauliflower, chopped
- 4 cups vegetable broth
- 1 cup unsweetened almond milk
- Salt and pepper, to taste
- Fresh chives, for garnish (optional)

**Directions:**

1. Heat olive oil in a large pot over medium heat. Add chopped onion and minced garlic, and cook until softened, about 5 minutes.
2. Add chopped cauliflower to the pot and cook for another 5 minutes.
3. Pour vegetable broth into the pot and bring to a simmer. Cook until cauliflower is tender, about 15-20 minutes.
4. Use an immersion blender to blend the soup until smooth. Alternatively, carefully transfer the soup to a blender and blend until smooth, then return to the pot.
5. Stir in unsweetened almond milk and season with salt and pepper to taste.
6. Serve the creamy cauliflower soup hot, garnished with fresh chives if desired.

**Nutritional Information (per serving):**

- Calories: 120
- Protein: 3g
- Fat: 5g
- Carbohydrates: 15g
- Fiber: 5g

# Tomato Basil Soup

Prep Time: 10 mins

Total Time: 30 mins

Servings: 4

**Ingredients:**

- 1 tablespoon olive oil
- 1 onion, chopped
- 2 cloves garlic, minced
- 2 cans (14 oz each) diced tomatoes
- 2 cups vegetable broth
- 1/4 cup fresh basil leaves, chopped
- Salt and pepper, to taste
- 1/4 cup plain Greek yogurt, for serving (optional)
- Fresh basil leaves, for garnish (optional)

**Directions:**

1. Heat olive oil in a large pot over medium heat. Add chopped onion and minced garlic, and cook until softened, about 5 minutes.

2. Add diced tomatoes (with their juices) and vegetable broth to the pot. Bring to a simmer and cook for 15 minutes.

3. Stir in chopped basil leaves and season with salt and pepper to taste.

4. Use an immersion blender to blend the soup until smooth. Alternatively, carefully transfer the soup to a blender and blend until smooth, then return to the pot.

5. Serve the tomato basil soup hot, with a dollop of plain Greek yogurt on top and garnished with fresh basil leaves if desired.

**Nutritional Information (per serving):**

- Calories: 100
- Protein: 3g
- Fat: 3g
- Carbohydrates: 16g
- Fiber: 5g

## Coconut Curry Lentil Soup

Prep Time: 15 mins

Total Time: 45 mins

Servings: 4

**Ingredients:**

- 1 tablespoon olive oil
- 1 onion, chopped
- 2 cloves garlic, minced
- 2 carrots, diced
- 2 celery stalks, diced
- 1 cup dry red lentils, rinsed
- 4 cups vegetable broth
- 1 can (14 oz) coconut milk

- 2 tablespoons curry powder
- Salt and pepper, to taste
- Fresh cilantro, for garnish (optional)
.

**Directions:**

1. Heat olive oil in a large pot over medium heat. Add chopped onion and minced garlic, and cook until softened, about 5 minutes.

2. Add diced carrots and diced celery to the pot, and cook for another 5 minutes.

3. Stir in dry red lentils, vegetable broth, coconut milk, and curry powder. Bring to a simmer and cook for 25-30 minutes, or until lentils are tender.

4. Taste and adjust seasoning if necessary.

5. Serve the coconut curry lentil soup hot, garnished with fresh cilantro if desired.

**Nutritional Information (per serving):**

- Calories: 320
- Protein: 13g
- Fat: 18g
- Carbohydrates: 31g
- Fiber: 15g

# Miso Mushroom Soup

Prep Time: 10 mins

Total Time: 25 mins

Servings: 4

**Ingredients:**

- 4 cups vegetable broth
- 2 cups water
- 4 ounces' shiitake mushrooms, sliced
- 4 ounces' button mushrooms, sliced
- 2 tablespoons miso paste
- 2 green onions, thinly sliced
- 1 tablespoon soy sauce
- 1 teaspoon sesame oil
- 1 teaspoon grated ginger
- 2 cloves garlic, minced
- Fresh cilantro, for garnish (optional)
- Red pepper flakes, for garnish (optional)

**Directions:**

1. In a large pot, bring vegetable broth and water to a simmer over medium heat.
2. Add sliced shiitake mushrooms and button mushrooms to the pot, and simmer for 10 minutes.
3. In a small bowl, whisk together miso paste and a ladleful of hot broth until smooth. Stir the miso mixture back into the pot.
4. Add thinly sliced green onions, soy sauce, sesame oil, grated ginger, and minced garlic to the pot. Simmer for an additional 5 minutes.
5. Taste and adjust seasoning if necessary.
6. Serve the miso mushroom soup hot, garnished with fresh cilantro and red pepper flakes if desired.

**Nutritional Information (per serving):**

- Calories: 70
- Protein: 4g
- Fat: 2g
- Carbohydrates: 10g
- Fiber: 2g

## Detox Lentil Soup

Prep Time: 15 mins

Total Time: 45 mins

Servings: 4

**Ingredients:**

- 1 tablespoon olive oil
- 1 onion, chopped
- 2 cloves garlic, minced
- 2 carrots, diced
- 2 celery stalks, diced
- 1 cup dry green lentils, rinsed
- 4 cups vegetable broth
- 1 teaspoon ground cumin
- 1 teaspoon ground turmeric
- Salt and pepper, to taste
- Fresh parsley, for garnish (optional)
- Lemon wedges, for serving (optional)

**Directions:**

1. Heat olive oil in a large pot over medium heat. Add chopped onion and minced garlic, and cook until softened, about 5 minutes.

2. Add diced carrots and diced celery to the pot, and cook for another 5 minutes.

3. Stir in dry green lentils, vegetable broth, ground cumin, and ground turmeric. Bring to a simmer and cook for 25-30 minutes, or until lentils are tender.

4. Taste and adjust seasoning if necessary.

5. Serve the detox lentil soup hot, garnished with fresh parsley and lemon wedges if desired.

**Nutritional Information (per serving):**

- Calories: 220
- Protein: 12g
- Fat: 4g
- Carbohydrates: 36g
- Fiber: 15g

# Creamy Cauliflower Soup

Prep Time: 10 mins

Total Time: 30 mins

Servings: 4

**Ingredients:**

- 1 tablespoon olive oil
- 1 onion, chopped
- 2 cloves garlic, minced
- 1 head cauliflower, chopped
- 4 cups vegetable broth
- 1 cup unsweetened almond milk
- Salt and pepper, to taste

- Fresh chives, for garnish (optional)

**Directions:**

1. Heat olive oil in a large pot over medium heat. Add chopped onion and minced garlic, and cook until softened, about 5 minutes.

2. Add chopped cauliflower to the pot and cook for another 5 minutes.

3. Pour vegetable broth into the pot and bring to a simmer. Cook until cauliflower is tender, about 15-20 minutes.

4. Use an immersion blender to blend the soup until smooth. Alternatively, carefully transfer the soup to a blender and blend until smooth, then return to the pot.

5. Stir in unsweetened almond milk and season with salt and pepper to taste.

6. Serve the creamy cauliflower soup hot, garnished with fresh chives if desired.

**Nutritional Information (per serving):**

- Calories: 120
- Protein: 3g
- Fat: 5g
- Carbohydrates: 15g
- Fiber: 5g

## Tomato Basil Soup

Prep Time: 10 mins

Total Time: 30 mins

Servings: 4

**Ingredients:**

- 1 tablespoon olive oil
- 1 onion, chopped
- 2 cloves garlic, minced
- 2 cans (14 oz each) diced tomatoes
- 2 cups vegetable broth
- 1/4 cup fresh basil leaves, chopped
- Salt and pepper, to taste
- 1/4 cup plain Greek yogurt, for serving (optional)
- Fresh basil leaves, for garnish (optional)

**Directions:**

1. Heat olive oil in a large pot over medium heat. Add chopped onion and minced garlic, and cook until softened, about 5 minutes.
2. Add diced tomatoes (with their juices) and vegetable broth to the pot. Bring to a simmer and cook for 15 minutes.
3. Stir in chopped basil leaves and season with salt and pepper to taste.
4. Use an immersion blender to blend the soup until smooth. Alternatively, carefully transfer the soup to a blender and blend until smooth, then return to the pot.
5. Serve the tomato basil soup hot, with a dollop of plain Greek yogurt on top and garnished with fresh basil leaves if desired.

**Nutritional Information (per serving):**

- Calories: 100
- Protein: 3g

- Fat: 3g
- Carbohydrates: 16g
- Fiber: 5g

## Coconut Curry Lentil Soup

Prep Time: 15 mins

Total Time: 45 mins

Servings: 4

**Ingredients:**

- 1 tablespoon olive oil
- 1 onion, chopped
- 2 cloves garlic, minced
- 2 carrots, diced
- 2 celery stalks, diced
- 1 cup dry red lentils, rinsed
- 4 cups vegetable broth
- 1 can (14 oz) coconut milk
- 2 tablespoons curry powder
- Salt and pepper, to taste
- Fresh cilantro, for garnish (optional)

**Directions:**

1. Heat olive oil in a large pot over medium heat. Add chopped onion and minced garlic, and cook until softened, about 5 minutes.

2. Add diced carrots and diced celery to the pot, and cook for another 5 minutes.

3. Stir in dry red lentils, vegetable broth, coconut milk, and curry powder. Bring to a simmer and cook for 25-30 minutes, or until lentils are tender.
4. Taste and adjust seasoning if necessary.
5. Serve the coconut curry lentil soup hot, garnished with fresh cilantro if desired.

**Nutritional Information (per serving):**

- Calories: 320
- Protein: 13g
- Fat: 18g
- Carbohydrates: 31g
- Fiber: 15g

# MEAL PLAN

*Day 1*

- **Breakfast:** Turmeric Latte
- **Lunch:** Mediterranean Quinoa Salad with Grilled Shrimp
- **Dinner:** Lemon Garlic Butter Shrimp with Turmeric Latte
- **Snack:** Green Tea Matcha Latte

*Day 2*

- **Breakfast:** Berry Blast Smoothie
- **Lunch:** Avocado Shrimp Salad with Cilantro Lime Dressing
- **Dinner:** Grilled Mahi-Mahi with Lemon Turmeric Sauce
- **Snack:** Turmeric Latte

*Day 3*

- **Breakfast:** Green Tea Matcha Latte
- **Lunch:** Microbiome Smoothie
- **Dinner:** Baked Cod with Turmeric Latte
- **Snack:** Berry Blast Smoothie

*Day 4*

- **Breakfast:** Turmeric Latte
- **Lunch:** Thai Shrimp Salad with Peanut Dressing
- **Dinner:** Grilled Lemon Herb Salmon with Turmeric Latte
- **Snack:** Green Tea Matcha Latte

*Day 5*

- **Breakfast:** Berry Blast Smoothie
- **Lunch:** Seared Scallop Caesar Salad
- **Dinner:** Spicy Baked Tilapia with Lemon Turmeric Sauce

- **Snack:** Turmeric Latte

*Day 6*

- **Breakfast:** Green Tea Matcha Latte
- **Lunch:** Microbiome Smoothie
- **Dinner:** Grilled Garlic Herb Shrimp with Turmeric Latte
- **Snack:** Berry Blast Smoothie

*Day 7*

- **Breakfast:** Turmeric Latte
- **Lunch:** Greek Salad with Grilled Chicken
- **Dinner:** Baked Salmon with Lemon Turmeric Sauce
- **Snack:** Green Tea Matcha Latte

*Day 8*

- **Breakfast:** Green Tea Matcha Latte
- **Lunch:** Microbiome Smoothie
- **Dinner:** Grilled Salmon with Turmeric Latte
- **Snack:** Berry Blast Smoothie

*Day 9*

- **Breakfast:** Turmeric Latte
- **Lunch:** Mixed Greens Salad with Grilled Shrimp
- **Dinner:** Baked Cod with Lemon Turmeric Sauce
- **Snack:** Green Tea Matcha Latte

*Day 10*

- **Breakfast:** Berry Blast Smoothie
- **Lunch:** Seared Tuna Salad with Avocado Dressing
- **Dinner:** Stir-Fried Garlic Shrimp with Turmeric Latte
- **Snack:** Turmeric Latte

*Day 11*

- **Breakfast:** Green Tea Matcha Latte
- **Lunch:** Microbiome Smoothie
- **Dinner:** Grilled Lemon Herb Salmon with Turmeric Latte
- **Snack:** Berry Blast Smoothie

*Day 12*

- **Breakfast:** Turmeric Latte
- **Lunch:** Greek Salad with Grilled Chicken
- **Dinner:** Spicy Baked Tilapia with Lemon Turmeric Sauce
- **Snack:** Green Tea Matcha Latte

*Day 13*

- **Breakfast:** Berry Blast Smoothie
- **Lunch:** Seared Scallop Salad with Citrus Dressing
- **Dinner:** Grilled Garlic Herb Shrimp with Turmeric Latte
- **Snack:** Turmeric Latte

*Day 14*

- **Breakfast:** Green Tea Matcha Latte
- **Lunch:** Microbiome Smoothie
- **Dinner:** Baked Salmon with Turmeric Latte
- **Snack:** Berry Blast Smoothie

# CONCLUSION

In conclusion, embarking on the journey of managing Exocrine Pancreatic Insufficiency (EPI) through dietary changes can be both challenging and rewarding. Throughout this guide, we've delved into the intricacies of the EPI diet, exploring its fundamental principles, essential ingredients, and kitchen tools, as well as an array of food options suitable for lean proteins, low-fat dairy, healthy carbohydrates, and fruits and vegetables.

Understanding EPI is the first step towards effectively managing its symptoms. By grasping the role of the pancreas in digestion and recognizing the challenges posed by EPI, individuals can take proactive steps to optimize their dietary choices and improve their quality of life. The EPI diet emphasizes consuming foods that are easy to digest, low in fat, and rich in essential nutrients, thereby alleviating digestive discomfort and promoting overall well-being.

Stocking your pantry with EPI-friendly ingredients and equipping your kitchen with the necessary tools can streamline meal preparation and enhance your culinary experience. With careful planning and creativity, you can transform simple, wholesome ingredients into delicious and nourishing meals that support your health goals.

Moreover, incorporating a diverse range of lean proteins, low-fat dairy, healthy carbohydrates, fruits, and vegetables into your diet ensures a balanced intake of vital nutrients, including protein, vitamins, minerals, and fiber. By prioritizing nutrient-dense foods and minimizing processed and high-fat options, individuals with EPI can maintain optimal nutrition while managing digestive symptoms.

As you navigate the complexities of the EPI diet, remember that progress takes time and patience. Be kind to yourself and celebrate each small victory along the way. Whether you're experimenting with new recipes, exploring unfamiliar ingredients, or simply making mindful choices at mealtime, every step forward contributes to your overall health and well-being.

In the words of Hippocrates, "Let food be thy medicine and medicine be thy food." As you embrace the transformative power of nutrition in managing EPI, remember that you hold the key to your own health journey. Stay resilient, stay committed, and never underestimate the profound impact that wholesome, nourishing food can have on your life.

So, as you continue on your path towards health and vitality, remember that each meal is an opportunity to nourish your body, support your well-being, and savor the joys of life to the fullest. Embrace the journey, embrace the nourishment, and let your health be your greatest motivation.

Made in the USA
Las Vegas, NV
24 October 2024

10435280R00125